GRADE 5

Curriculum Units

Measuring Polygons

2-D Geometry and Measurement

UNIT 5

Parrot Fire Kris Northern

"Rather than zoom into the fractal you can zoom into the edge of it and continually find the same pattern repeating itself much like the shoreline of a lake viewed from a plane."– **Kris Northern**

Investigations
IN NUMBER, DATA, AND SPACE®

Measuring Polygons

2-D Geometry and Measurement

UNIT 5

Power Polygons™ is a trademark of ETA/Cuisenaire®.

Use of the trademark or company name implies no relationship, sponsorship, endorsement, sale, or promotion on the part of Pearson Education, Inc., or its affiliates.

Glenview, Illinois • Boston, Massachusetts
Chandler, Arizona • Upper Saddle River, New Jersey

The Investigations curriculum was developed by TERC, Cambridge, MA.

This material is based on work supported by the National Science Foundation ("NSF") under Grant No. ESI-0095450. Any opinions, findings, and conclusions or recommendations expressed in this material are those of the author(s) and do not necessarily reflect the views of the National Science Foundation.

ISBN-13: 978-0-328-60042-7

ISBN-10: 0-328-60042-3

1 2 3 4 5 6 7 8 9 10 V003 14 13 12 11 10

T E R C

Co-Principal Investigators

Susan Jo Russell

Karen Economopoulos

Authors

Lucy Wittenberg
Director Grades 3–5

Karen Economopoulos
Director Grades K–2

Virginia Bastable
(SummerMath for Teachers,
Mt. Holyoke College)

Katie Hickey Bloomfield

Keith Cochran

Darrell Earnest

Arusha Hollister

Nancy Horowitz

Erin Leidl

Megan Murray

Young Oh

Beth W. Perry

Susan Jo Russell

Deborah Schifter
(Education
Development Center)

Kathy Sillman

Administrative Staff

Amy Taber
Project Manager

Beth Bergeron

Lorraine Brooks

Emi Fujiwara

Contributing Authors

Denise Baumann

Jennifer DiBrienza

Hollee Freeman

Paula Hooper

Jan Mokros

Stephen Monk
(University of Washington)

Mary Beth O'Connor

Judy Storeygard

Cornelia Tierney

Elizabeth Van Cleef

Carol Wright

Technology

Jim Hammerman

Classroom Field Work

Amy Appell

Rachel E. Davis

Traci Higgins

Julia Thompson

Collaborating Teachers

This group of dedicated teachers carried out extensive field testing in their classrooms, met regularly to discuss issues of teaching and learning mathematics, provided feedback to staff, welcomed staff into their classrooms to document students' work, and contributed both suggestions and written material that has been incorporated into the curriculum.

Bethany Altchek	Maura McGrail
Linda Amaral	Kathe Millett
Kimberly Beauregard	Florence Molyneaux
Barbara Bernard	Amy Monkiewicz
Nancy Buell	Elizabeth Monopoli
Rose Christiansen	Carol Murray
Chris Colbath-Hess	Robyn Musser
Lisette Colon	Christine Norrman
Kim Cook	Deborah O'Brien
Frances Cooper	Timothy O'Connor
Kathleen Drew	Anne Marie O'Reilly
Rebeka Eston Salemi	Mark Paige
Thomas Fisher	Margaret Riddle
Michael Flynn	Karen Schweitzer
Holly Ghazey	Elisabeth Seyferth
Susan Gillis	Susan Smith
Danielle Harrington	Debra Sorvillo
Elaine Herzog	Shoshanah Starr
Francine Hiller	Janice Szymaszek
Kirsten Lee Howard	Karen Tobin
Liliana Klass	JoAnn Trauschke
Leslie Kramer	Ana Vaisenstein
Melissa Lee Andrichak	Yvonne Watson
Kelley Lee Sadowski	Michelle Woods
Jennifer Levitan	Mary Wright
Mary Lou LoVecchio	
Kristen McEnaney	

Note: Unless otherwise noted, all contributors listed above were staff of the Education Research Collaborative at TERC during their work on the curriculum. Other affiliations during the time of development are listed.

Advisors

Deborah Lowenberg Ball,
University of Michigan

Hyman Bass, Professor of Mathematics and Mathematics Education
University of Michigan

Mary Canner, Principal, Natick Public Schools

Thomas Carpenter, Professor of Curriculum and Instruction,
University of Wisconsin-Madison

Janis Freckmann, Elementary Mathematics Coordinator,
Milwaukee Public Schools

Lynne Godfrey, Mathematics Coach,
Cambridge Public Schools

Ginger Hanlon, Instructional Specialist in Mathematics,
New York City Public Schools

DeAnn Huinker, Director, Center for Mathematics and
Science Education Research, University of Wisconsin-Milwaukee

James Kaput, Professor of Mathematics, University of
Massachusetts-Dartmouth

Kate Kline, Associate Professor, Department of Mathematics
and Statistics, Western Michigan University

Jim Lewis, Professor of Mathematics,
University of Nebraska-Lincoln

William McCallum, Professor of Mathematics,
University of Arizona

Harriet Pollatsek, Professor of Mathematics,
Mount Holyoke College

Debra Shein-Gerson, Elementary Mathematics Specialist,
Weston Public Schools

Gary Shevell, Assistant Principal,
New York City Public Schools

Liz Sweeney, Elementary Math Department,
Boston Public Schools

Lucy West, Consultant, Metamorphosis:
Teaching Learning Communities, Inc.

This revision of the curriculum was built on the work of the many authors who contributed to the first edition (published between 1994 and 1998). We acknowledge the critical contributions of these authors in developing the content and pedagogy of *Investigations*:

Authors

Joan Akers

Michael T. Battista

Douglas H. Clements

Karen Economopoulos

Marlene Kliman

Jan Mokros

Megan Murray

Ricardo Nemirovsky

Andee Rubin

Susan Jo Russell

Cornelia Tierney

Contributing Authors

Mary Berle-Carman

Rebecca B. Corwin

Rebeka Eston

Claryce Evans

Anne Goodrow

Cliff Konold

Chris Mainhart

Sue McMillen

Jerrie Moffet

Tracy Noble

Kim O'Neil

Mark Ogonowski

Julie Sarama

Amy Shulman Weinberg

Margie Singer

Virginia Woolley

Tracey Wright

Contents

UNIT 5

Measuring Polygons

INTRODUCTION AND OVERVIEW

INVESTIGATION 1

Polygons: Names, Properties, and Angles

INVESTIGATION 2

Finding Perimeter and Area of Related Rectangles

INVESTIGATION 3

Similarity

Investigations

CURRICULUM

Overview of Program Components

The **Curriculum Units** are the teaching guides. (See far right.)

Implementing Investigations in Grade 5 offers suggestions for implementing the curriculum. It also contains a comprehensive index.

The **Differentiation and Intervention Guide** offers additional activities for each Investigation to support the range of learners.

Investigations for the Interactive Whiteboard provides whole-class instructional support to enhance each session.

The **Resource Masters and Transparencies CD** contains all reproducible materials that support instruction.
The **LogoPaths CD** provides an environment in which students investigate a variety of geometric ideas. It is formally introduced in this unit.

FOR STUDENTS

The **Student Activity Book** contains the consumable student pages (Recording Sheets, Homework, Practice, and so on).

The **Student Math Handbook** contains Math Words and Ideas pages and Games directions.

The *Investigations* Curriculum

Investigations in Number, Data, and Space® is a K–5 mathematics curriculum designed to engage students in making sense of mathematical ideas. Six major goals guided the development of the *Investigations in Number, Data, and Space*® curriculum. The curriculum is designed to:

- Support students to make sense of mathematics and learn that they can be mathematical thinkers

- Focus on computational fluency with whole numbers as a major goal of the elementary grades

- Provide substantive work in important areas of mathematics—rational numbers, geometry, measurement, data, and early algebra—and connections among them

- Emphasize reasoning about mathematical ideas

- Communicate mathematics content and pedagogy to teachers

- Engage the range of learners in understanding mathematics

Underlying these goals are three guiding principles that are touchstones for the *Investigations* team as we approach both students and teachers as agents of their own learning:

1. *Students have mathematical ideas.* Students come to school with ideas about numbers, shapes, measurements, patterns, and data. If given the opportunity to learn in an environment that stresses making sense of mathematics, students build on the ideas they already have and learn about new mathematics they have never encountered. Students learn that they are capable of having mathematical ideas, applying what they know to new situations, and thinking and reasoning about unfamiliar problems.

2. *Teachers are engaged in ongoing learning* about mathematics content, pedagogy, and student learning. The curriculum provides material for professional development, to be used by teachers individually or in groups, that supports teachers' continued learning as they use the curriculum over several years. The *Investigations* curriculum materials are designed as much to be a dialogue with teachers as to be a core of content for students.

3. *Teachers collaborate with the students and curriculum materials* to create the curriculum as enacted in the classroom. The only way for a good curriculum to be used well is for teachers to be active participants in implementing it. Teachers use the curriculum to maintain a clear, focused, and coherent agenda for mathematics teaching. At the same time, they observe and listen carefully to students, try to understand how they are thinking, and make teaching decisions based on these observations.

Investigations is based on experience from research and practice, including field testing that involved documentation of thousands of hours in classrooms, observations of students, input from teachers, and analysis of student work. As a result, the curriculum addresses the learning needs of real students in a wide range of classrooms and communities. The investigations are carefully designed to invite all students into mathematics—girls and boys; members of diverse cultural, ethnic, and language groups; and students with a wide variety of strengths, needs, and interests.

Based on this extensive classroom testing, the curriculum takes seriously the time students need to develop a strong conceptual foundation and skills based on that foundation. Each curriculum unit focuses on an area of content in depth, providing time for students to develop and practice ideas across a variety of activities and contexts that build on each other. Daily guidelines for time spent on class sessions, Classroom Routines (K–3), and Ten-Minute Math (3–5) reflect the commitment to devoting adequate time to mathematics in each school day.

About This Curriculum Unit

This **Curriculum Unit** is one of nine teaching guides in Grade 5. The fifth unit in Grade 5 is *Measuring Polygons*.

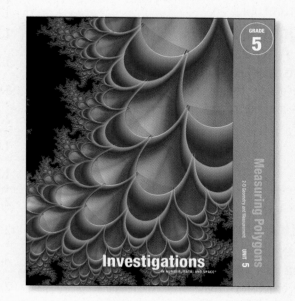

- The **Introduction and Overview** section organizes and presents the instructional materials, provides background information, and highlights important features specific to this unit.

- Each Curriculum Unit contains several **Investigations.** Each Investigation focuses on a set of related mathematical ideas.

- Investigations are divided into one-hour **Sessions,** or lessons.

- Sessions have a combination of these parts: **Activity, Discussion, Math Workshop, Assessment Activity,** and **Session Follow-Up.**

- Each session also has one or more **Ten-Minute Math** activities that are done outside of math time.

- At the back of the book is a collection of **Teacher Notes** and **Dialogue Boxes** that provide professional development related to the unit.

- Also included at the back of the book are the **Student Math Handbook** pages for this unit.

- The **Index** provides a way to look up important words or terms.

Overview

O F   T H I S   U N I T

Investigation	Session	Day	
INVESTIGATION 1 **Polygons: Names, Properties, and Angles** Students classify polygons by looking at attributes including number of sides, lengths of sides, and sizes of angles. They find the measures of angles using Power Polygons.	**1.1** Triangles	1	
	1.2 Quadrilaterals	2	
	1.3 Relationships Among Quadrilaterals	3	
	1.4 Regular Polygons	4	
	1.5 Angles Sizes in Polygons	5	
	1.6 Examining Angles and Classifying Polygons	6	
	1.7 Assessment: Quadrilaterals and Angles	7	
INVESTIGATION 2 **Finding Perimeter and Area of Related Rectangles** Students build sequences of related polygons in order to learn about area, perimeter, and the relationship between them.	**2.1** A Sequence of Squares	8	
	2.2 Doubling Dimensions of Squares	9	
	2.3 Building a Sequence of Rectangles	10	
	2.4 Different Perimeter, Same Area	11	
	2.5 Measuring Rectangles	12	
	2.6 Assessment: Perimeter and Area of Rectangles	13	
INVESTIGATION 3 **Similarity** Students investigate figures that are mathematically similar to some of the Power Polygons, noting the relationship between side length and the area of similar figures.	**3.1** Building Similar Polygons	14	
	3.2 Building More Similar Shapes	15	
	3.3 Building More Similar Shapes, *continued*	16	
	3.4 Similarity Posters	17	
	3.5 End-of-Unit Assessment	18	

Each *Investigations* session has some combination of these five parts: **Activity, Discussion, Math Workshop, Assessment Activity,** and **Session Follow-Up.** These session parts are indicated in the chart below. Each session also has one **Ten-Minute Math** activity that is done outside of math time.

 (W) Interactive Whiteboard

Activity	Discussion	Math Workshop	Assessment Activity	Session Follow-Up
(W) (W)	●			●
(W) ●	(W)			●
	(W)	●		●
	(W)	●		●
(W) ● ●				●
	(W)	●		●
		●	●	●
● ●	(W)			●
	(W)	●		●
●	(W)			●
(W) ●	(W) ●			●
(W)		●		●
	(W)	●	●	●
(W) ●	(W)			●
(W) ●		●		●
	(W)	●		●
	(W)	●		●
●			●	●

Ten-Minute Math

Quick Images: 2-D	Quick Survey
(W)	
(W)	
(W)	
(W)	
(W)	
(W)	
(W)	
	(W)
	(W)
(W)	
(W)	
	(W)
	(W)
(W)	
(W)	
	(W)
	(W)
	(W)

Mathematics

Measuring Polygons is the second Grade 5 unit in the geometry and measurement strand of *Investigations*. These units develop ideas about the attributes of 2-dimensional (2-D) and 3-dimensional (3-D) shapes, as well as how these attributes determine classification. They also develop ideas about linear measurement (which includes perimeter), area, the measurement of angles, and volume.

LOOKING BACK The work in this unit assumes students have had experience with perimeter, including measuring around both irregular shapes and familiar shapes such as rectangles. It also assumes students know the distinction between measuring area with square units and measuring length with linear units such as inches. This unit builds on previous work with classifying shapes as polygons, triangles, and quadrilaterals. The work with angles in this unit assumes that students are familiar with right (90 degree) angles and that they understand the way an angle can be built by joining two smaller angles.

This unit focuses on 4 Mathematical Emphases:

1 Features of Shape Describing and classifying two-dimensional figures

Math Focus Points

◆ Identifying attributes of polygons

◆ Describing triangles by the sizes of their angles and the lengths of their sides

◆ Using attributes to describe and compare quadrilaterals including parallelograms, rectangles, rhombuses, and squares

◆ Defining a regular polygon as a polygon with all sides and all angles equal

Geometric definitions are based on grouping a set of figures that have a common attribute. Since the attributes that apply to grouping quadrilaterals (e.g., having four right angles, having four sides of the same length, or having two

pairs of parallel sides) are independent, some quadrilaterals fit more than one category and therefore have more than one term that apply. For example, the characteristics of a square include having four sides of the same length and having four right angles; therefore, a square is also a rhombus (a quadrilateral with four sides of the same length) and a rectangle (a quadrilateral with four right angles).

In Investigation 1, students examine characteristics of various polygons. These include descriptions of triangles, attributes of a regular polygon, and the relationships among quadrilaterals. They consider questions such as the following: Are all squares rectangles? Are all rectangles parallelograms? If all squares are rhombuses, then are all rhombuses squares? Considering questions like these helps students begin to make sense of a seemingly confusing hierarchical classification for geometric figures.

2 Features of Shape Describing and measuring angles

Math Focus Points

◆ Using known angles to find the measures of other angles

One attribute of a geometric figure is the size of its angles. Angles are measured in terms of degrees—an indication of an amount of turning. A full turn is considered 360 degrees. A common benchmark for angle measure is a right angle, which is a fourth of a full turn, or 90 degrees. In Investigation 1, students explore angle size, beginning with the idea that a square or rectangle contains right angles.

```
┌ 90°                           90° ┐
│                                   │
│                                   │
│                                   │
│                                   │
└ 90°                           90° ┘
```

The measures of angles in a polygon can be determined by fitting together known angle measures.

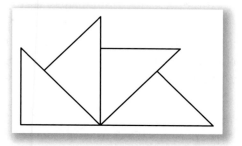

Comparing angle sizes provides one means for determining angle measures. For instance, if three copies of a certain angle fit together to form a right angle, then each of the smaller angles must be $\frac{1}{3}$ of 90 degrees, or 30 degrees. In this unit, students measure angles of 30, 45, 60, 90, 120, and 150 degrees by fitting together smaller angles and reasoning about the size of the angles they form.

3 Linear and Area Measurement Finding perimeter and area of rectangles

Math Focus Points

◆ Comparing the perimeters and areas of rectangles when the dimensions are multiplied by given amounts

◆ Using numerical and/or geometric patterns to describe how the perimeters and areas of rectangles change when the dimensions change

◆ Using representations to explain how perimeters and areas of rectangles change

◆ Creating different rectangles with the same area but different perimeters

◆ Understanding square units as a unit of measure

◆ Creating different rectangles with the same perimeter but different areas

◆ Describing the shapes of rectangles that have the same area or the same perimeter

The distance around the outside of a two-dimensional shape is called the perimeter. The amount of space that a given object covers is called the area. Although both perimeter and area are related to the shape of a rectangle, changes to the shape of a rectangle can affect one of the measures and not the other. For instance, if a rectangle is cut in half horizontally and then the two pieces are moved and reconnected to make a new rectangle, the area of the original shape is maintained. No area is gained or lost; however, the perimeter has been changed.

In Investigation 2, students work with rectangles to calculate perimeter and area. In addition, they examine situations in which two rectangles with the same perimeter have different areas and two rectangles with the same areas have different perimeters. This work highlights the key mathematical idea that perimeter and area are two different, independent types of measurement. Perimeter is a 1-dimensional (or linear) measure, and area is a 2-dimensional measure. These measurements are considered independent because changing the shape of a rectangle does not necessarily result in a change to both the perimeter and the area; in fact, it is possible to change one of the measures, while keeping the other the same.

4 Features of Shape Creating and describing similar shapes

Math Focus Points

◆ Recognizing and building similar figures

◆ Examining the relationship among angles, line lengths, and areas of similar polygons

◆ Making a generalization about the changes in area of similar figures

◆ Building similar figures for polygons made from two or more Power Polygon pieces

◆ Using Power Polygons™ to find the areas of similar hexagons

Although perimeter and area are independent measures, there are some geometric transformations that do imply a relationship between the perimeter and the area of the original and the transformed figure. One such transformation is similarity. Two figures are similar to each other when one is a proportional enlargement of the other.

These two figures have identical angles, but one figure is larger than the other. Scale drawings, maps, blueprints, and photographic enlargements are everyday examples everyday of similarity relationships. In Investigation 3, students use Power Polygons to build and draw sequences of similar figures.

If a given rectangle is enlarged so that each dimension is multiplied by the same factor, then the perimeter of the enlarged figure is also multiplied by that factor, and the area of the enlarged figure is multiplied by that factor squared. For example, consider a 4-inch by 6-inch rectangle and a second rectangle that is formed by doubling the dimensions of the first. The resulting rectangle will be 8 inches by 12 inches:

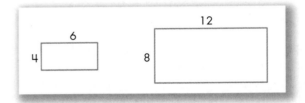

The perimeter of the larger rectangle is 40 inches, or double the perimeter of the smaller one. The area of the larger rectangle is 96 square inches, which is four (2×2) times larger. In Investigation 3, students examine these relationships between the perimeters and areas of similar figures.

Ten-Minute Math activities focus on

◆ Decomposing images of 2-D shapes and then recombining them to make a given design

◆ Developing language and concepts to communicate about spatial relationships

◆ Organizing and analyzing visual images

◆ Describing features of the data

◆ Interpreting and posing questions about the data

LOOKING FORWARD

In future years, students refine their understanding of classification of geometric shapes as they develop a deeper sense of the critical attributes that define a shape. The work with angles continues as students encounter and use tools such as protractors and angle measurers. With these tools, students are able to extend the variety of sizes of angles they can measure.

Student ideas about perimeter and area from this unit are the building blocks for understanding the formulas for calculating these measures for a variety of shapes. In addition, work on examining similar figures from this unit is the basis for a more formal study of both congruence and similarity.

Technology Note

Introducing the Software The *LogoPaths* software is introduced to students in this unit. If you are planning to use the software, you will need to familiarize yourself with it. For information about the *LogoPaths* software, refer to the *Software Support Reference Guide* found on the CD. To prepare to integrate this work into your classroom and to manage the computer environment, see **Teacher Note:** Introducing and Managing the *LogoPaths* Software, page 139, and **Teacher Note:** About the Mathematics in the *LogoPaths* Software, page 141, for further support and information.

Assessment

ONGOING ASSESSMENT: Observing Students at Work

The following sessions provide **Ongoing Assessment: Observing Students at Work** opportunities:

- **Session 1.1, p. 26**
- **Session 1.2, p. 33**
- **Session 1.3, pp. 40, 41, and 42**
- **Session 1.4, p. 48**
- **Session 1.5, pp. 53–54**
- **Session 1.6, p. 60**

- **Session 1.7, p. 63**
- **Session 2.1, p. 73**
- **Session 2.2, pp. 78 and 79**
- **Session 2.3, p. 85**
- **Session 2.4, pp. 91 and 93**
- **Session 2.5, pp. 98 and 99**

- **Session 2.6, p. 104**
- **Session 3.1, p. 112**
- **Session 3.2, pp. 119–120, 121, and 123**
- **Session 3.3, p. 128**
- **Session 3.5, p. 134**

WRITING OPPORTUNITIES

The following sessions have **writing** opportunities for students to explain their mathematical thinking:

- **Session 1.1, p. 27**
  Student Activity Book, pp. 1–2

- **Session 1.3, pp. 40, 41, and 44**
  Student Activity Book, pp. 8–10, 12

- **Session 1.5, pp. 52–53**
  Student Activity Book, pp. 17–19

- **Session 2.1, pp. 73, 75**
  Student Activity Book, pp. 27, 29

- **Session 2.2, p. 77**
  Student Activity Book, pp. 31–32

- **Session 2.3, pp. 84–85**
  Student Activity Book, pp. 35–36

- **Session 2.4, p. 90**
  Student Activity Book, p. 39

- **Session 2.5, pp. 97–98**
  Student Activity Book, pp. 43–44

- **Session 3.1, p. 110**
  Student Activity Book, p. 49

- **Session 3.2, p. 120**
  Student Activity Book, p. 54

- **Session 3.3, p. 126**
  Student Activity Book, p. 57

- **Session 3.5, pp. 134–135**
  M20 and M22, End-of-Unit Assessment

PORTFOLIO OPPORTUNITIES

The following sessions have work appropriate for a **portfolio:**

- **Session 1.5, p. 52**
  Student Activity Book, pp. 17–19

- **Session 1.7, p. 63**
  M17, Assessment: Quadrilaterals and Angles

- **Session 2.3, pp. 84–85**
  Student Activity Book, pp. 35–36

- **Session 2.6, p. 103**
  M19, Assessment: Perimeter and Area of Rectangles

- **Session 3.5, pp. 134–135**
  M20–M22, End-of-Unit Assessment

Assessing the Benchmarks

Observing students as they engage in conversation about their ideas is a primary means to assess their mathematical understanding. Consider all of your students' work, not just the written assessments. See the chart below for suggestions about key activities to observe.

See the **Differentiation and Intervention Guide** for quizzes that can be used after each Investigation.

[handwritten] ＊ Outlined w/examples in Parent letter＊

Benchmarks in This Unit	Key Activities to Observe	Assessment
1. Identify different quadrilaterals by attribute, and know that some quadrilaterals can be classified in more than one way. *[handwritten] ＊see Pg.138 Teacher note.*	**Session 1.3:** Classifying Polygons	**Session 1.7 Assessment Activity:** Quadrilaterals and Angles **Session 3.5 End-of-Unit Assessment:** Problem 1
2. Use known angle sizes to determine the sizes of other angles (30°, 45°, 60°, 90°, 120°, and 150°).	**Session 1.5:** Angles in the Power Polygons	**Session 1.7 Assessment Activity:** Quadrilaterals and Angles **Session 3.5 End-of-Unit Assessment:** Problem 1
3. Determine the perimeter and area of rectangles.	**Session 2.3:** A Sequence of Rectangles **Session 2.5:** Fencing a Garden	**Session 2.6 Assessment Activity:** Perimeter and Area of Rectangles **Session 3.5 End-of-Unit Assessment:** Problem 2
4. Identify mathematically similar polygons. *[handwritten crossed out] Not Doing this.*	**Sessions 3.3 and 3.4:** Similarity Posters	**Session 3.5 End-of-Unit Assessment:** Problem 3

Relating the Mathematical Emphases to the Benchmarks

Mathematical Emphases	Benchmarks
Features of Shape Describing and Classifying Two-dimensional Figures	1
Features of Shape Describing and Measuring Angles	2
Linear and Area Measurement Finding perimeter and area	3
Features of Shape Creating and describing similar figures	4

Ten-Minute Math

Ten-Minute Math offers practice and review of key concepts for this grade level. These daily activities, to be done in ten minutes outside of math class, are introduced in a unit and repeated throughout the grade. Specific directions for the day's activity are provided in each session. For the full description and variations of each classroom activity, see *Implementing Investigations in Grade 5*.

Activity	Introduced	Full Description of Activity and Its Variations
Quick Images: 2-D	Unit 1, Session 1.1	*Implementing Investigations in Grade 5*
Quick Survey	Unit 5, Session 2.1 (this unit)	*Implementing Investigations in Grade 5*

Quick Images: 2-D

Students visualize and analyze images of 2-D geometric figures. After briefly viewing an image of a 2-D design, students draw it from the mental image they formed during the brief viewing.

Math Focus Points

◆ Organizing and analyzing visual images

◆ Developing language and concepts needed to communicate about spatial relationships

◆ Decomposing images of 2-D shapes and then recombining them to make a given design

Quick Survey

Students collect, display, describe, and interpret data about themselves or something they can observe easily. Students describe what they can tell from the data, generate some new questions and, if appropriate, make predictions about what will happen the next time they collect the same data.

Math Focus Points

◆ Describing features of the data

◆ Interpreting and posing questions about the data

Practice and Review

Practice and review play a critical role in the *Investigations* program. The following components and features are available to provide regular reinforcement of key mathematical concepts and procedures.

Books	Features	In This Unit ...
Curriculum Unit	**Ten-Minute Math** offers practice and review of key concepts for this grade level. These daily activities, to be done in ten minutes outside of math class, are introduced in a unit and repeated throughout the grade. Specific directions for the day's activity are provided in each session. For the full description and variations of each classroom activity, see *Implementing Investigations in Grade 5.*	• All sessions
Student Activity Book	**Daily Practice** pages in the *Student Activity Book* provide one of three types of written practice: **reinforcement** of the content of the unit, **ongoing review,** or **enrichment** opportunities. Some Daily Practice pages will also have Ongoing Review items with multiple-choice problems similar to those on standardized tests.	• All sessions
	Homework pages in the *Student Activity Book* are an extension of the work done in class. At times they help students prepare for upcoming activities.	• Session 1.1 • Session 2.3 • Session 1.3 • Session 2.4 • Session 1.4 • Session 2.6 • Session 1.5 • Session 3.1 • Session 1.7 • Session 3.2 • Session 2.1 • Session 3.3 • Session 2.2 • Session 3.4
Student Math Handbook	**Math Words and Ideas** in the *Student Math Handbook* are pages that summarize key words and ideas. Most Words and Ideas pages have at least one exercise.	• **Student Math Handbook , pp. 93–104**
	Games pages are found in a section of the *Student Math Handbook.*	• **No games are introduced in this unit.**

Supporting the Range of Learners

The **Differentiation and Intervention Guide** provides Intervention, Extension, and Practice activities for use within each Investigation.

Sessions	1.1	1.3	1.4	1.5	1.6	1.7	2.1	2.2	2.3	2.4	2.5	2.6	3.1	3.2	3.3	3.5
Intervention		•	•	•	•	•	•	•	•	•	•	•		•	•	•
Extension		•		•		•	•	•	•	•	•		•	•	•	
ELL	•							•	•				•		•	

Intervention

Suggestions are made to support and engage students who are having difficulty with a particular idea, activity, or problem.

Extension

Suggestions are made to support and engage students who finish early or may be ready for additional challenge.

English Language Learners (ELL)

In this unit, students work with a variety of two- and three-dimensional shapes, and begin to describe and classify features such as angles, perimeter, and area. Because the unit introduces a number of new mathematical terms, English Language Learners may need additional support as they incorporate these new words into their vocabularies.

You can help English Language Learners by creating a chart with a list of shape names (*circle, square, triangle, rectangle, etc.*) and a visual representation of each shape. You can create a chart that is big enough to hang in the classroom, or help students make their own charts to be used on an individual basis. Encourage English Language Learners to draw shapes as they learn their names and features.

Hands-on activities will be especially useful to English Language Learners as they learn about *perimeter, area,* and *length.* Try to incorporate manipulatives into the

activities whenever possible, and give these students special opportunities to practice describing, measuring, and calculating information about shapes. Previewing the material with English Language Learners will help them participate more fully in subsequent discussions with the whole class.

A number of activities ask students to compare different shapes. While English Language Learners may be familiar with some comparative words (*larger, smaller, longer, wider*), they will benefit from one-on-one or small group work that allows them to use these words in context. As a simple exercise, you can give students shapes of different sizes and ask them to compare them, providing linguistic support as necessary.

Working with the Range of Learners: Classroom Cases is a set of episodes written by teachers that focuses on meeting the needs of the range of learners in the classroom. In the first section, *Setting up the Mathematical Community,* teachers write about how they create a supportive and productive learning environment in their classrooms. In the next section, *Accommodations for Learning,* teachers focus on specific modifications they make to meet the needs of some of their learners. In the last section, *Language and Representation,* teachers share how they help students use representations and develop language to investigate and express mathematical ideas. The questions at the end of each case provide a starting point for your own reflection or for discussion with colleagues. See *Implementing Investigations in Grade 5* for this set of episodes.

Mathematical Emphases

Features of Shape Describing and classifying two-dimensional figures

Math Focus Points

◆ Identifying attributes of polygons

◆ Describing triangles by the sizes of their angles and the lengths of their sides

◆ Using attributes to describe and compare quadrilaterals including parallelograms, rectangles, rhombuses, and squares

◆ Defining a regular polygon as a polygon with all sides and all angles equal

Features of Shape Describing and measuring angles

Math Focus Points

◆ Using known angles to find the measures of other angles

Polygons: Names, Properties, and Angles

	Student Activity Book	Student Math Handbook	Professional Development: Read Ahead of Time	
SESSION 1.1 p. 24				
Triangles Students sort triangles by attributes that include angle size and side length. They use geometric vocabulary to describe different types of triangles.	1–4	95	• **Teacher Note:** Classification of Triangles and Quadrilaterals, p. 137 • **Part 4: Ten-Minute Math** in *Implementing Investigations in Grade 5:* Quick Images	
SESSION 1.2 p. 31				
Quadrilaterals Students sort quadrilaterals by attributes that include angle size, side length, and the number of parallel sides. They are introduced to a *LogoPaths* activity that helps them understand the supplementary relationship between turning angles and the interior angles formed by those turns.	5–7	96–98	• **Teacher Note:** Introducing and Managing the *LogoPaths* Software, p. 139 • **Teacher Note:** About the Mathematics in the *LogoPaths* Software, p. 141 • **Software Support:** Read the directions for the *Angle and Turn Game* in the *Software Support Reference Guide* found on the software CD.	
SESSION 1.3 p. 39				
Relationships Among Quadrilaterals Students continue to classify polygons. They consider and discuss the relationships among the following quadrilaterals: parallelogram, rhombus, rectangle, and square.	8–12	96–98		

Ten-Minute Math See page 16 for an overview.

Quick Images: 2-D

- T54–T57, *Quick Images: 2-D* 🖳 Cut apart the cards and set aside Images 1–14 for this Investigation.

Materials to Gather	Materials to Prepare
• **Blank transparency**	• **T58–T59, Shape Cards** 🖳 Cut apart the Shape Cards, and set aside cards 1 and 4 for this session. • **M9–M10, Shape Cards** Have students cut apart the Shape Cards ahead of time. Have students put their initials on their cards and store them in an envelope or resealable plastic bag. (1 deck per pair) • **Chart paper** Write the title "Ways to Describe Triangles" at the top and write the headings "Angle Sizes" and "Side Lengths". • **M11–M12, Family Letter** Make copies. (1 per student)
• **Shape Cards** (from Session 1.1) • **T58–T59, Shape Cards** 🖳 (from Session 1.1) Use quadrilateral cards 20, 21, 23, 24, and 25 for this session.	• **Chart paper** Write the title "Types of Quadrilaterals" at the top, and create four columns labeled "Square," "Rectangle," "Rhombus," and "Parallelogram." Draw a sketch of each figure in the appropriate column. • **M13–M14, Family Letter** Make copies. (1 per student) • *Angle and Turn Game* Read the directions in the *Software Support Reference Guide,* and prepare for demonstrating this game by marking a circle on the floor using chalk or masking tape. There should be enough space around the circle for the student to walk five steps away from it in a straight line. (optional) • **Projector and computer with *LogoPaths* software installed** (optional)
• **Shape Cards** (from Session 1.1)	• **Computers with *LogoPaths* software installed** (1 per pair; optional) • **Chart paper** Write the title "Relationships Among Quadrilaterals" at the top, and list the following statements: a. _____ rectangles are parallelograms. b. _____ rectangles are squares. c. _____ parallelograms are rectangles. d. _____ squares are rectangles. e. _____ rhombuses are squares.

🖳 Overhead Transparency

Polygons: Names, Properties, and Angles, *continued*

	Student Activity Book	Student Math Handbook	Professional Development: Read Ahead of Time	
SESSION 1.4 p. 45				
Regular Polygons Students identify regular polygons as polygons that have all equal sides and all equal angles. They are also introduced to Power Polygons.	13–15	93–94		
SESSION 1.5 p. 50				
Angle Sizes in Polygons Students determine the sizes of the angles in Power Polygons using right angles and other known angle measurements as landmarks.	17–21	99–101	• **Teacher Note:** The Rule of 180°, p. 142	
SESSION 1.6 p. 57				
Examining Angles and Classifying Polygons Students discuss their strategies for finding angle measures. In Math Workshop, they continue to find more angle sizes, sort polygons based on a variety of attributes, and draw triangles using the *LogoPaths* software.	17–19, 23	93, 95, 96–98, 99–101	• **Dialogue Box:** Finding Angle Measures of Power Polygons, p. 163	
SESSION 1.7 p. 62				
Assessment: Quadrilaterals and Angles Students are assessed on their understanding of the relationships among quadrilaterals and their ability to find the measures of angles.	17–19, 24–25	95, 96–98, 99–101	• **Teacher Note:** Assessment: Quadrilaterals and Angles, p. 143	

Materials to Gather	Materials to Prepare
• **M15, Power Polygons** • **T61, Polygons: Regular and Not Regular** 🖨	• **Power Polygons** For each small group of three or four students, place a variety of shapes in a pie plate or plastic container. These will also be used in Investigation 3. • **Computers with *LogoPaths* software installed** (1 per pair; optional)
• **Power Polygons** (8 of shape D for class demonstration plus a variety of shapes for each pair) • **Blank transparencies**	• **Computers with *LogoPaths* software installed** (1 per pair; optional)
• **Power Polygons** • **Shape Cards** (from Session 1.1)	• **M1, *LogoPaths: Triangles*** Make copies. (1 per student; optional) • **Computers with *LogoPaths* software installed** (1 per pair; optional)
• **Power Polygons** • **Shape Cards** (from Session 1.1) • **M1, *LogoPaths: Triangles*** (from Session 1.6; optional)	• **M17, Assessment: Quadrilaterals and Angles** Make copies. (1 per student) • **Computers with *LogoPaths* software installed** (1 per pair; optional)

🖨 Overhead Transparency

Triangles

Math Focus Points

◆ Identifying attributes of polygons

◆ Describing triangles by the sizes of their angles and the lengths of their sides

Vocabulary

right
acute
obtuse
equilateral
scalene
isosceles

Today's Plan		Materials
1 ACTIVITY **Triangles: Two the Same, One Different**	35 MIN · CLASS · PAIRS	• *Student Activity Book*, pp. 1–2 • M9–M10; T58–T59*
2 DISCUSSION **Describing Triangles**	15 MIN · CLASS	• Chart: "Ways to Describe Triangles"*
3 ACTIVITY **Introducing *Guess My Rule***	10 MIN · CLASS · GROUPS	• Shape Cards (from Activity 1); T58–T59 (from Activity 1) • Blank transparency
4 SESSION FOLLOW-UP **Daily Practice and Homework**		• *Student Activity Book*, pp. 3–4 • *Student Math Handbook*, p. 95 • M11–M12, Family Letter*

*See *Materials to Prepare*, p. 21.

Ten-Minute Math

Quick Images: 2-D Show Images 1 and 2 of *Quick Images: 2-D* (T54) one at a time and follow the procedure for the basic routine. For each image, students discuss how they drew their figures, including any revisions they made after each viewing.

Ask students:

• How did you remember the parts of the image?

• What did you notice about the relationship of the parts of the image?

• What helped you remember the whole image so that you could draw your design?

ACTIVITY

1 Triangles: Two the Same, One Different

35 MIN   CLASS   PAIRS

In this activity, students compare two triangles to determine a common characteristic. After writing down this characteristic, students draw three additional triangles—two that share this characteristic and one that does not.❶ The sets of triangles generated by this work serve as material for the whole class discussion on identifying terms used to describe triangles.❷

Find triangles 1 and 4 in your transparency set of Shape Cards (T58–T59), and display them on the overhead.

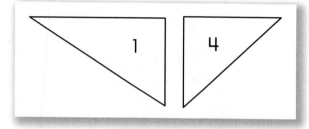

How are these triangles the same?

Give students a minute to talk to a neighbor, and then solicit their responses.

Some may say that these triangles have right angles; others may name the angles as 90 degrees. Use this as an opportunity to remind students that both are correct. Also remind them that they can check to see whether an angle is a right angle (or 90 degrees) by comparing it with the corner of a sheet of paper.

Can you imagine another triangle that would fit this characteristic? Turn to a neighbor and draw such a triangle on paper. Now think about a triangle that would not *fit this description.*

Teaching Note

❶ **Decks of Shape Cards** To participate in this activity, each pair of students shares one deck of Shape Cards. These should be cut apart before the session begins.

Professional Development

❷ **Teacher Note:** Classification of Triangles and Quadrilaterals, p. 137

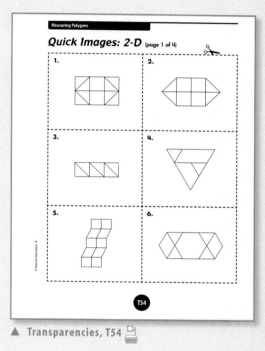

▲ Transparencies, T54

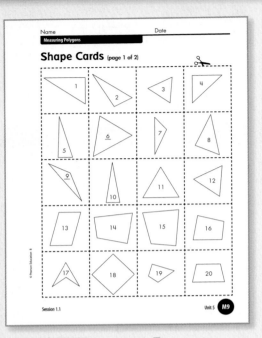

▲ Resource Masters, M9; T58

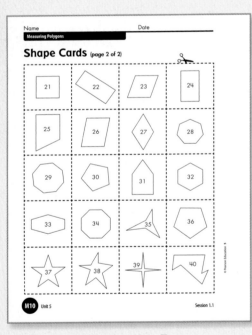

▲ Resource Masters, M10; T59

Ask one or two students to draw on the whiteboard a triangle that does not have a right angle. If two students offer the same kind of triangle (either with all angles less than 90 degrees or with one angle greater than 90 degrees), ask if anyone can draw a triangle that is different but still not a right triangle.

Have students separate the triangle cards (cards 1 through 12) from their own sets of Shape Cards that they cut apart earlier from Shape Cards (M9–M10). Ask students to work with a partner to find pairs of triangles that have an attribute in common. Complete the activity by having students draw two more triangles that share that attribute and one that does not. Direct them to record their work on *Student Activity Book* pages 1 and 2.

Triangles: Two the Same, One Different gives students practice identifying and describing attributes shared by pairs of triangles

ONGOING ASSESSMENT: Observing Students at Work

Students sort triangles by attributes that include angle size and side length.

- **What attributes of the triangles are students using for their grouping?** Do they use lengths of sides, size of angles, or both?

- **What terms do students use to describe triangles?** Are students describing angles as acute or obtuse? Are they describing triangles as equilateral, isosceles, or scalene?

As you circulate among students, look for examples of groupings using size of angles and length of sides, as this will be the focus of the following discussion. Also, note the vocabulary that students use to describe the features of the triangles. Besides right angles, fifth graders should be noticing angles that are acute (less than 90 degrees) and angles that are obtuse (greater than 90 degrees), although they may not remember these particular terms from their work in Grade 4. They should also be able to recognize equilateral triangles (all sides are the same length), scalene triangles (all sides are different lengths), and isosceles triangles (two sides are the same length). Identify pairs of students who come up with examples of these attributes, and ask them to be prepared to participate in the discussion.

DISCUSSION

2 Describing Triangles

15 MIN   CLASS

Math Focus Points for Discussion

◆ Describing triangles by the size of their angles and the lengths of their sides

Show the chart you prepared titled "Ways to Describe Triangles" with the subheadings "Angle Sizes" and "Side Lengths." Ask the pairs of students you identified in the activity to present their sets of triangles (four that share an attribute and one that does not). Have the students who are presenting ask the class to identify the characteristic that groups together the first four and excludes the last one. As students present, ask the class to tell you the subheading under which each set of triangles belongs. This will help students recognize that these are two ways of classifying triangles—by angle size and by side length.❸

For example, students might have identified cards #2 and #7 and drawn figures such as these:

Sample Student Work

Name		Date
Measuring Polygons		

Triangles: Two the Same, One Different (page 1 of 2)

In your set of Shape Cards, find two triangles that have some attribute in common. Write the numbers of these triangles and answer the questions below.

1. Triangles # _____ and _____

   What is the same about these two? _____
   _____

   Draw two other triangles that fit with these two.

   Draw a triangle that is different. Explain how it is different.

2. Triangles # _____ and _____

   What is the same about these two? _____
   _____

   Draw two other triangles that fit with these two.

   Draw a triangle that is different. Explain how it is different.

Session 1.1   Unit 5 **1**

▲ **Student Activity Book, pp. 1–2**   WRITING

Differentiation

❸ **English Language Learners** To participate in this activity, students must be able to use math-related terms such as *angle*, *degrees*, *length*, *side(s)*, *right*, *obtuse*, *equilateral*, and *scalene*. You can support English Language Learners by previewing a list of relevant words before the presentations. Give each English Language Learner a copy of the list so that he or she can keep track of the new terms. You can help English Language Learners practice using each word by having them draw pictures of triangles and then asking questions about them. Point to one side of your triangle. How do we measure the length of each side? Now point to an angle. Is that an obtuse angle? How can we tell if the angle is more or less than 90°?

Students might say:

"One angle is more than 90 degrees."

"One angle is bigger than a right angle."

Students may also use the term "obtuse angle." When one of the geometric terms is introduced, write it on the chart and provide time for students to ask questions. If students do not offer all of the terms (which is particularly likely for terms that describe side length, such as *scalene* and *isosceles*), introduce the rest of the terms, and write them on the chart next to the description. For example:

Some of you may remember that there is a word for triangles that have all sides of the same length. These are called *equilateral* triangles. But these triangles that [Alicia] and [Zachary] showed us have no sides that are the same length. Triangles like this also have a special name; they are called *scalene* triangles.

Collect and record the descriptions and geometric terms about angle sizes first, followed by the descriptions and terms for side lengths. Post the completed chart in the room so that students may refer to it as they work.

A completed chart should include the following information:

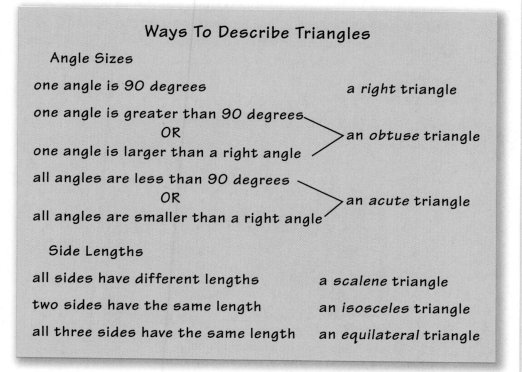

Ways To Describe Triangles

Angle Sizes

one angle is 90 degrees — a *right* triangle

one angle is greater than 90 degrees
OR
one angle is larger than a right angle
— an *obtuse* triangle

all angles are less than 90 degrees
OR
all angles are smaller than a right angle
— an *acute* triangle

Side Lengths

all sides have different lengths — a *scalene* triangle

two sides have the same length — an *isosceles* triangle

all three sides have the same length — an *equilateral* triangle

ACTIVITY

3 Introducing *Guess My Rule*

10 MIN   CLASS   GROUPS

For the last ten minutes of the session, introduce students to the game *Guess My Rule,* which they continue to play throughout this investigation. Students may remember this game from their work in previous grades.

You may remember other versions of *Guess My Rule*. In this version, one person thinks of a rule and, without telling anyone the rule, places two of the Shape Cards that fit the rule on a sheet of paper. The person then picks one Shape Card that does not fit the rule and places it off the paper. The other players take turns choosing a new card that they think either fits the rule or does not fit the rule. Once you think you know what the rule is, you can say that you want to tell the rule.

To demonstrate the game, draw a large rectangle on a blank transparency to represent the sheet of paper. Choose a rule, such as "has an obtuse angle," and, without telling students the rule, place two transparency Shape Cards that fit this rule in the rectangle on the overhead. Place one card that does not fit the rule outside of the rectangle. (Use the whole

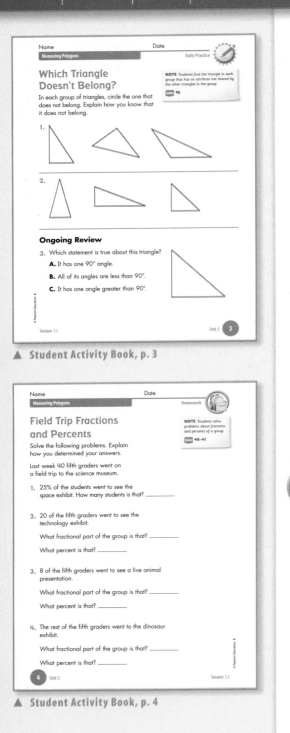

▲ Student Activity Book, p. 3

▲ Student Activity Book, p. 4

deck of Shape Cards for this game, not just the triangle cards.) Play a round of *Guess My Rule* with the class to familiarize them with this version of the game. If there is time, students may then play *Guess My Rule* in groups of three or four with their own decks of Shape Cards. Each group will need a sheet of paper on which to place their polygons that "fit the rule."

A teacher demonstrates the game Guess My Rule.

SESSION FOLLOW-UP

4 Daily Practice and Homework

 Daily Practice: For reinforcement of this unit's content, have students complete *Student Activity Book* page 3.

 Homework: On *Student Activity Book* page 4, students solve problems about fractions and percents of a group.

 Student Math Handbook: Students and families may use *Student Math Handbook* page 95 for reference and review. See pages 170–173 in the back of this unit.

Family Letter: Send home copies of the Family Letter (M11–M12).

Quadrilaterals

Math Focus Points

◆ Identifying attributes of polygons

◆ Using attributes to describe and compare quadrilaterals including parallelograms, rectangles, rhombuses, and squares

Vocabulary

quadrilateral	rectangle
parallel	rhombus
trapezoid	square
parallelogram	supplementary

Today's Plan / Materials

Today's Plan		Materials
① ACTIVITY **Quadrilaterals: Two the Same, One Different**	40 MIN CLASS PAIRS	• *Student Activity Book*, pp. 5–6 • Shape Cards (from Session 1.1)
② DISCUSSION **What Rules Fit?**	20 MIN CLASS	• T58–T59 (from Session 1.1) • Shape Cards (from Session 1.1); Chart: "Types of Quadrilaterals"*
③ ACTIVITY **Introducing *LogoPaths* Activity: *Angle and Turn Game* (optional)**	CLASS	• Projector and Computer with *LogoPaths* software installed
④ SESSION FOLLOW-UP **Daily Practice**		• *Student Activity Book*, p. 7 • *Student Math Handbook*, pp. 96–98 • M13–M14, Family Letter*

*See *Materials to Prepare,* p. 21.

Ten-Minute Math

Quick Images: 2-D Show Images 3 and 4 of *Quick Images: 2-D* (T54) one at a time and follow the procedure for the basic routine. For each image, students discuss how they drew their figures, including any revisions they made after each viewing.

Ask students:

• How did you remember the parts of the image?

• What did you notice about the relationship of the parts of the image?

• What helped you remember the whole image so that you could draw your design?

ACTIVITY

1 Quadrilaterals: Two the Same, One Different

40 MIN   CLASS   PAIRS

In this activity, students compare two quadrilaterals to determine a common characteristic. After writing down this characteristic, students then draw three additional quadrilaterals—two that share this characteristic and one that does not. Students may consider characteristics such as having four right angles, having exactly two sides parallel, and having all sides the same length.

The sets of quadrilaterals generated by this work serve as material for the whole class discussion on naming types of quadrilaterals and listing their properties.

In the last session, you worked with triangle cards. Today we are going to do a similar activity working with quadrilateral cards. In your Shape Cards set, find the quadrilaterals that are shapes 20 and 25 [both trapezoids]. How are they the same? Talk to your neighbor for a minute until you agree on something that is the same about these quadrilaterals.

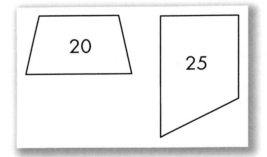

Allow a minute for students to share their ideas with each other. Having worked with quadrilaterals in Grades 3 and 4, students are likely to know the names of these quadrilaterals as well as attributes such as "right angles" or "parallel lines." Ask several students to share their ideas with the whole class, and write their responses on the board or overhead.

Students might say:

"They have a pair of parallel sides."

"They are both trapezoids."

After each suggestion, ask students to say whether or not they agree and why. If students suggest incorrect responses such as "They are both parallelograms," continue asking whether students agree, and solicit comments until agreement is reached.

Now you are going to look at some other quadrilaterals to see whether you can find other pairs that share something in common. As you work, you will draw two more examples of quadrilaterals that fit each rule and one example of a quadrilateral that does not fit.

Have students look at all of the quadrilaterals in the Shape Cards set (cards 13 through 27). As they did with the triangles, have students work with a partner to find pairs of quadrilaterals that have some attribute in common. Complete the activity by directing students to draw two more quadrilaterals that share that attribute and one that does not. Have them record their work on *Student Activity Book* pages 5–6.

ONGOING ASSESSMENT: Observing Students at Work

Students sort quadrilaterals by attributes that include angle size, side length, and number of parallel sides.

- **What attributes of the quadrilaterals are students using for their grouping?** Do they notice attributes such as all right angles, all sides of the same length, exactly two sides parallel, or two pairs of parallel sides?

- **What terms do students use to describe quadrilaterals?** Do they correctly name quadrilaterals using terms such as rectangle, parallelogram, trapezoid, rhombus, or square?

DISCUSSION

2 What Rules Fit?

20 MIN   CLASS

Math Focus Points for Discussion

◆ Using attributes to describe and compare quadrilaterals including parallelograms, rectangles, rhombuses, and squares

---

Name _____ **Date** _____

Measuring Polygons

Quadrilaterals: Two the Same, One Different (page 1 of 2)

In your set of Shape Cards, find two quadrilaterals that have some attribute in common. Write the numbers of these quadrilaterals and answer the questions below.

1. Quadrilaterals # _____ and _____
   What is the same about these two? _____

   Draw two other quadrilaterals that fit with these two.

   Draw a quadrilateral that is different. Explain how it is different.

2. Quadrilaterals # _____ and _____
   What is the same about these two? _____

   Draw two other quadrilaterals that fit with these two.

   Draw a quadrilateral that is different. Explain how it is different.

Session 1.2   Unit 5   5

▲ Student Activity Book, p. 5

Name _____ **Date** _____

Measuring Polygons

Quadrilaterals: Two the Same, One Different (page 2 of 2)

In your set of Shape Cards, find two quadrilaterals that have some attribute in common. Write the numbers of these quadrilaterals and answer the questions below.

3. Quadrilaterals # _____ and _____
   What is the same about these two? _____

   Draw two other quadrilaterals that fit with these two.

   Draw a quadrilateral that is different. Explain how it is different.

4. Quadrilaterals # _____ and _____
   What is the same about these two? _____

   Draw two other quadrilaterals that fit with these two.

   Draw a quadrilateral that is different. Explain how it is different.

6   Unit 5   Session 1.2

▲ Student Activity Book, p. 6

Bring the class together, and display the transparencies of quadrilaterals 21 (square) and 24 (rectangle) (T59) on the overhead.

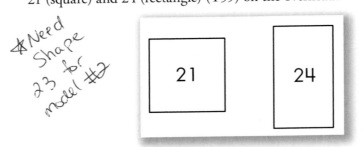

Need Shape 23 for model #2

Here are two quadrilaterals that I've grouped together. Look in your own set of Shape Cards and find one or two more shapes that you think fit with these two.

Give students a minute to do this and then solicit several responses. Find the quadrilaterals that students suggest in your set of transparency Shape Cards and put these on the overhead with the first two.

As students discuss, look for students who select a nonrectangular parallelogram as another shape that fits the rule.

Who can tell us what "rule" I might have used to group these two quadrilaterals? . . . Does each of these shapes that you added fit the same rule?

While it is likely that many students will choose "all right angles" as the attribute for these two shapes (and therefore choose other rectangles), these two shapes are also both parallelograms, having two pairs of parallel sides. If any student chooses a nonrectangular parallelogram, challenge the class to think about whether the first two quadrilaterals could fit more than one rule.

Many of you thought that my rule was "all right angles," and you chose rectangles to go with my two shapes. But [Joshua], you thought about it differently, because the shape you gave us doesn't have all right angles, and yet it still fits with my two shapes. Can you tell us what rule you were thinking about? . . . Who remembers what quadrilaterals that have two pairs of parallel sides are called? *(parallelograms)* . . . So is it possible that shapes can fit more than one rule? Can squares and rectangles also be parallelograms?

Give students a few minutes to discuss this, and then remove shape 24 (rectangle) and replace it with shape 23 (rhombus).

What if I started with these two instead? Are they both rectangles? . . . Why not? . . . Are they both parallelograms? . . . Is there any other attribute that they have in common? . . . Who remembers what quadrilaterals that have all sides of the same length are called? *(rhombuses)* . . . So which rules apply to this set of shapes?

As students consider these questions, they encounter the idea that the types of quadrilaterals include overlapping descriptors. In other words, a square is also a rhombus, a rectangle, and a parallelogram. Each term has a specific meaning and refers to a specific attribute, but a given quadrilateral can fit more than one description. In the next session, students work on the relationships among these terms, continuing to develop the idea that a single figure can have more than one attribute and thus more than one name.❶

For the last five minutes or so of this discussion, show students the chart you prepared titled "Types of Quadrilaterals." With the students' help, list characteristics of each quadrilateral on the chart under the sketches you made. A completed chart should include the following information:

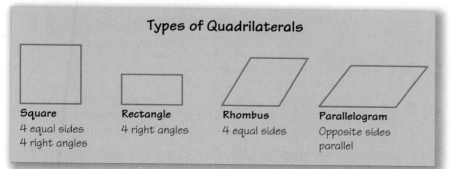

Types of Quadrilaterals

Square
4 equal sides
4 right angles

Rectangle
4 right angles

Rhombus
4 equal sides

Parallelogram
Opposite sides
parallel

Math Note

❶ **Different Names For the Same Figure** One of the first attributes of polygons that students consider in elementary school is number of sides. This gives polygons the names that students call these shapes (triangles, quadrilaterals, pentagons, hexagons, etc.). By this classification, each of these figures is distinct; no figure can be both a hexagon and also a pentagon. Some students bring this sense that a geometric term must be distinct to their work with quadrilaterals. In Grade 4, they began to examine the idea that some quadrilaterals can be described in different ways when they considered the relationship between squares and rectangles. In this investigation, they continue that work to include other types of quadrilaterals.

Professional Development

❷ **Teacher Note:** Introducing and Managing the *LogoPaths* Software, p. 139

❸ **Teacher Note:** About the Mathematics in the *LogoPaths* Software, p. 141

Technology Note

❹ **Working with the *LogoPaths* Software** For instructions and a complete description of the *LogoPaths* software, see the *Software Support Reference Guide* found on the software CD.

Math Note

❺ **Relating Turning Angles to Inside Angles of Polygons** Playing *Angle and Turn Game* prepares students for the work of drawing triangles, rhombuses, and parallelograms in later sessions of this unit by helping them understand the relationship between turns and the interior angles formed by those turns. As students use the *LogoPaths* software to draw polygons with angles other than 90°, they must pay attention to this relationship. For example, to create an interior angle of 60° for an equilateral triangle, students must turn the turtle 120°. In other words, the turn must be the supplement of the interior angle they wish to form; 120° and 60° are supplementary angles because together they form 180°, or a straight line. Students have been doing this each time they turned the turtle 90° while drawing squares and rectangles. However, since the interior angle created was also 90°, the relationship was not so readily apparent.

ACTIVITY

③ Introducing *LogoPaths* Activity: *Angle and Turn Game*

CLASS

Angle and Turn Game is played in pairs. The version you are introducing in this session focuses on supplementary angles. As the game begins, the turtle turns randomly and moves away from the point of origin. One player then enters a turn angle. The second player then attempts to enter the angle that will get the turtle pointing back to the origin. For example, if the first player enters a right turn of 35°, the second player then enters the supplementary right turn of 145°, resulting in a total turn of 180°. ❷ ❸ ❹ ❺ ❻ *This is only for logopaths so not really necessary.*

Demonstrate the game by asking a student volunteer to stand in the small circle you marked on the classroom floor. Have the student turn to face any direction, and then walk five steps in a straight line away from the circle.

The teacher selects a student to demonstrate the Angle and Turn Game *by walking a path the turtle might take.*

We can call this circle a "starting point" or "point of origin." How many degrees would [Terrence] have to turn in order to face the starting point again? Think about how many degrees you turn the turtle when you want to reverse your path in the games *Feed the Turtle* and *Mazes.*

Students should recognize that a turn of 180° reverses the student's direction.

In the game I am teaching you today, *Angle and Turn Game*, the turtle starts by turning randomly on its starting point and then moving away in a straight line. The object of the game is to use two turns to get the turtle back to the point of origin. Let's start the game and watch this first step.

Open *Angle and Turn Game* in the *LogoPaths* software by clicking on it once.

Angle and Turn Game is played in pairs. The first player enters a command that turns the turtle *partway* back towards the point of origin. The second player's job is to figure out how much more the turtle needs to turn to get all the way back to the starting point. What command could we enter to turn the turtle *partway* back?

Take a suggestion from a student volunteer and enter it on the computer—for example, right 35°.

The turtle turned back 35° towards the point of origin. The second player's job is to figure out how much more the turtle needs to turn to get all the way back to the starting point. Look at the picture on the computer screen. Can you see the turn that the turtle still needs to make?

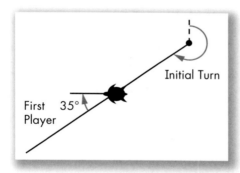

Have a student point out the remaining angle on the computer screen, and ask for a suggestion about what command to enter. While some students may recognize that the second player needs to enter a turn of 145° to complete the turn of 180°, that move may not yet be evident to all students. Enter whatever amount is suggested.

Math Note

⑥ **Other Combinations of Turns to Get Back to the Point of Origin** While the version of *Angle and Turn Game* taught in this session focuses on the use of supplementary angles, other combinations of 2 turns can be used to get the turtle back to the point of origin. For example, the second player could enter a command that undoes the first command and add an additional 180° turn in the same direction. For example, if Player 1 enters the command rt 35, Player 2 might enter **LT 215** (35° + 180°). Players can also enter more turns of more than 360° on either of the moves. For example, Player 1 might enter a command of **RT 420** (360° + 60°). Player 2 could then enter a command of **RT 120** or **RT 480** (360° + 120°) to get the turtle back to the point of origin.

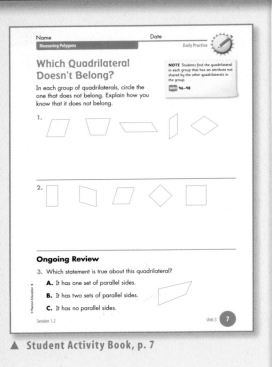

▲ Student Activity Book, p. 7

The turtle will turn the second amount and move forward in the new direction. If the suggested turn completes the 180°, the turtle will return to the point of origin and a message will appear announcing the student's success.

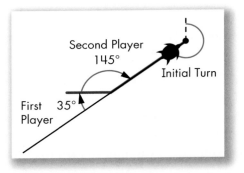

If the suggested turn does not complete 180° or results in a turn greater than 180°, a message appears telling the student the degrees by which the turtle is off. For example, a second turn of 135° results in the following message: "The turtle is off by 10 degrees." The same message appears if the student enters a second turn command of 155° and turns 10° too far.

Regardless of whether the turtle returns to the origin, students can click *cancel* to view their turns. Demonstrate this and use the opportunity to have students determine whether the second turn created a total turn of greater than or less than 180°.

SESSION FOLLOW-UP

 4 Daily Practice

 Daily Practice: For reinforcement of this unit's content, have students complete *Student Activity Book* page 7.

 Student Math Handbook: Students and families may use *Student Math Handbook* pages 96–98 for reference and review. See pages 170–173 in the back of this unit.

Family Letter: Send home copies of the Family Letter (M13–M14).

Relationships Among Quadrilaterals

Math Focus Points

◆ Using attributes to describe and compare quadrilaterals including parallelograms, rectangles, rhombuses, and squares

◆ Identifying attributes of polygons

Vocabulary

convex
Venn diagram

Today's Plan

		Materials
MATH WORKSHOP **① Classifying Polygons** **①A** Some Figures Have Many Names **①B** Guess My Rule **①C** LogoPaths: Angle and Turn Game (optional)	40 MIN	**①A** • Student Activity Book, pp. 8–10 **①B** • Shape Cards (from Session 1.1) **①C** • Computers with LogoPaths software installed
DISCUSSION **② Relationships Among Quadrilaterals**	20 MIN CLASS	• Chart: "Relationships Among Quadrilaterals"*
SESSSION FOLLOW-UP **③ Daily Practice and Homework**		• Student Activity Book, pp. 11–12 • Student Math Handbook, pp. 96–98

*See Materials to Prepare, p. 21.

Ten-Minute Math

Quick Images: 2-D Show Images 5 and 6 of *Quick Images: 2-D* (T54) one at a time and follow the procedure for the basic routine. For each image, students discuss how they drew their figures, including any revisions they made after each viewing.

Ask students:

• How did you remember the parts of the image?

• What did you notice about the relationship of the parts of the image?

• What helped you remember the whole image so that you could draw your design?

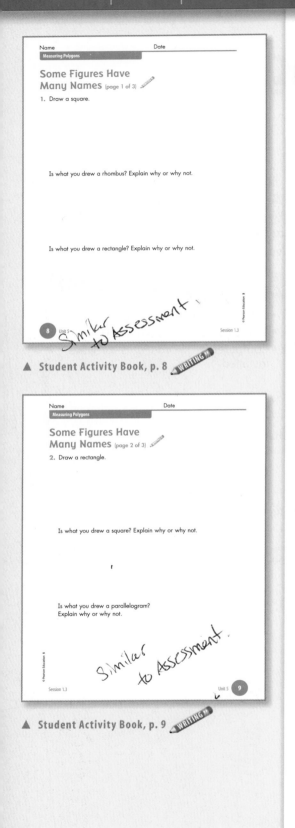

▲ Student Activity Book, p. 8

▲ Student Activity Book, p. 9

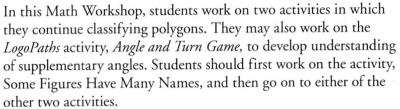

① Classifying Polygons

40 MIN

In this Math Workshop, students work on two activities in which they continue classifying polygons. They may also work on the *LogoPaths* activity, *Angle and Turn Game,* to develop understanding of supplementary angles. Students should first work on the activity, Some Figures Have Many Names, and then go on to either of the other two activities.

①A Some Figures Have Many Names

PAIRS

On *Student Activity Book* pages 8–10, students work in pairs to draw figures that fit the definition of a specific quadrilateral and examine what additional terms apply. Problem 4 may be unfamiliar to some students, so you may decide to spend a few minutes at the beginning of the session to be sure they understand what is being asked. The whole-group discussion at the end of the session should include the answers to all five of the statements in question, so make sure at least one pair of students is working on every statement. Ask one or more pairs of students to focus on any neglected statements.

ONGOING ASSESSMENT: Observing Students at Work

Students draw figures that fit the definition of a specific quadrilateral and examine what additional terms apply.

- **Do students' responses show the overlapping definitions?**
  For instance, do they explain how a square is a rhombus?

- **Do students' explanations include examples and nonexamples?**
  For instance, in explaining how some parallelograms are rectangles, do they draw some parallelograms that are rectangles and others that are not?

DIFFERENTIATION: Supporting the Range of Learners

(Intervention) Rather than draw figures, some students may find it easier to use the Shape Cards to locate figures with a given property.

(Intervention) If students are having difficulty writing their explanations, suggest that they ask a partner to write down a sentence or two while they give their explanation aloud. Student pairs may then work together to revise those sentences and make a written explanation.

1B Guess My Rule

GROUPS

This game was introduced in Grade 4 and reintroduced in Session 1.1. In this activity, students sort and classify polygons according to various attributes by playing *Guess My Rule* with the Shape Cards. Possible categories include the number of sides, the lengths of the sides, the size of the angles, and whether or not the figure is convex. Students practice the geometric terms from the first two sessions as they play.

Not that impt.

Working in small groups, students take turns choosing a rule and guessing what the rule is by looking carefully at the cards. First, one student thinks of a rule. Then, *without telling the rule,* he or she places two cards with shapes that fit the rule on a sheet of paper and one card with a shape that does not fit the rule off the paper. The other players then take turns choosing a new card that they think either fits the rule or does not fit the rule. The player thinking of the rule then places the new card in the correct location. Any student who knows the rule may state it. If it is not correct, students continue to choose and place new cards until the correct rule is identified.

ONGOING ASSESSMENT: Observing Students at Work

Students sort polygons by various attributes, including number of sides, side length, and angle size.

- **Do students use a variety of attributes in making their rules, including side length and angle size?**

- **Do students use geometric terms to describe their rules?**

As students play the game, ask them to explain what attribute they are using to group their cards. If they use informal language, ask them whether they know the geometric term for the attribute or property they have chosen.

DIFFERENTIATION: Supporting the Range of Learners

Intervention Some students may find it helpful to use the rules that are written on the class poster as suggestions or as rules to modify. For example, you might say to a student, "I see a couple of rules that include parallel sides. Choose a shape that has some parallel sides, and think of a rule that describes that shape." One such rule would be shapes with two sets of parallel sides.

Extension For students who need a challenge, define the terms *regular* and *convex*, and suggest that they use one of these attributes to group the polygons.

Some Figures Have Many Names (page 3 of 3)

3. Draw a parallelogram, a rectangle, a rhombus, and a square.

4. Write *All, Some,* or *No* to complete these statements:
   a. _____ rectangles are parallelograms.
   b. _____ rectangles are squares.
   c. _____ parallelograms are rectangles.
   d. _____ squares are rectangles.
   e. _____ rhombuses are squares.

5. Choose one of the sentences in Problem 4 and explain your response. Include drawings to show what you mean.

▲ Student Activity Book, p. 10

1C *LogoPaths: Angle and Turn Game* (optional)

PAIRS

Pairs of students play *Angle and Turn Game*, in which one player enters a command to turn the turtle partway back toward its point of origin. The second player must then enter a command to finish turning the turtle toward the origin. For complete details about this activity, see Session 1.2, pages 36–38.

If you have a limited number of computers available in your classroom, pairs of students can cycle through the computer activities, just as they cycle through the other Math Workshop activities.

ONGOING ASSESSMENT: Observing Students at Work

Students develop an understanding of supplementary angles as they use knowledge of 180° as a half turn to reverse the direction of the turtle in two turns.

- **Do students demonstrate understanding that a total turn of 180° will return the turtle to the point of origin?**

- **Are the pairs of students able to identify the correct supplementary angle in each round of the game?** For example, if Player 1 enters 55°, does Player 2 enter 125°, the supplement of that angle?

DIFFERENTIATION: Supporting the Range of Learners

Extension Encourage students who demonstrate a good understanding of supplementary angles to challenge themselves by turning the turtle more than a complete turn on either or both of the moves. For example, Player 1 might enter a command of **RT 390** (360° + 30°). Player 2 could then enter a command of **RT 150** or **RT 510** (360° + 150°) to get the turtle back to the point of origin.

DISCUSSION

② Relationships Among Quadrilaterals

20 MIN   CLASS

Math Focus Points for Discussion

◆ Using attributes to describe and compare quadrilaterals including parallelograms, rectangles, rhombuses, and squares

Show the chart you prepared with the five statements from question 4 on *Student Activity Book* pages 8–10. Begin the discussion by soliciting answers to all five questions. Focus the class discussion on the first two statements. Have the student pairs that worked on the first statement describing the relationship between rectangles and parallelograms offer their explanations and their supporting drawings to the class. After each pair shares, ask the class whether they have any questions for the group.

Students might say:

"A rectangle has two pairs of parallel sides, and so that makes it a parallelogram."

"You can't have a rectangle without having parallel sides."

"The right angles in a rectangle make the sides go parallel."

After the student comments for the first statement have been discussed, move on to the second statement.

Student Activity Book, p. 11

Student Activity Book, p. 12

Students might say:

"A rectangle has to have four right angles. If the rectangle also has sides that are all the same, it is a square. If it has sides that are not all the same, it is only a rectangle."

"Rectangle tells you about the angles—that they are all right angles. It doesn't say anything about the sides. The sides might be the same or they might be different."

A completed chart should look like this:

Relationships Among Quadrilaterals

a. __All__ rectangles are parallelograms.

b. __Some__ rectangles are squares.

c. __Some__ parallelograms are rectangles.

d. __All__ squares are rectangles.

e. __Some__ rhombuses are squares.

You can decide whether your class will benefit from examining a Venn diagram approach to illustrate the relationships among parallelograms, rectangles, rhombuses, and squares.

SESSION FOLLOW-UP

3 Daily Practice and Homework

 Daily Practice: For ongoing review, have students complete *Student Activity Book* page 11.

 Homework: Students describe attributes of a square and a rectangle and what distinguishes the two shapes, on *Student Activity Book* page 12.

Student Math Handbook: Students and families may use *Student Math Handbook* pages 96–98 for reference and review. See pages 170–173 in the back of this unit.

Regular Polygons

Vocabulary
regular
hexagon
heptagon
octagon
pentagon
decagon

Math Focus Points

◆ Defining a regular polygon as a polygon with all sides and all angles equal

◆ Identifying attributes of polygons

Today's Plan		Materials
DISCUSSION ❶ **Regular Polygons**	20 MIN CLASS	• M15, M16/T61 • Power Polygons*; pie plates or plastic containers (optional)
MATH WORKSHOP ❷ **Working With Power Polygons** ②Ⓐ *Which Are Regular Polygons?* ②Ⓑ *Guess My Rule* with Power Polygons ②Ⓒ *LogoPaths: Angle and Turn* (optional)	40 MIN	②Ⓐ • *Student Activity Book*, p. 13 • Power Polygons* ②Ⓑ • Power Polygons* ②Ⓒ • Computers with *LogoPaths* software installed
SESSION FOLLOW-UP ❸ **Daily Practice and Homework**		• *Student Activity Book*, pp. 14–15 • *Student Math Handbook*, pp. 93–94

*See *Materials to Prepare*, p. 23.

Ten-Minute Math

Quick Images: 2-D Show Images 7 and 8 of *Quick Images: 2-D* (T55) one at a time and follow the procedure for the basic routine. For each image, students discuss how they drew their figures, including any revisions they made after each viewing.

Ask students:

• How did you remember the parts of the image?

• What did you notice about the relationship of the parts of the image?

• What helped you remember the whole image so that you could draw your design?

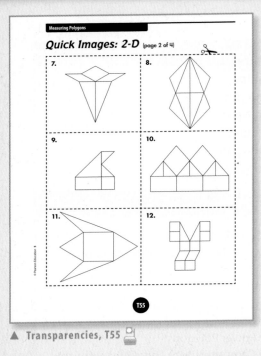

Measuring Polygons

Quick Images: 2-D (page 2 of 4)

7.

8.

9.

10.

11.

12.

T55

▲ **Transparencies, T55**

Teaching Note

❶ **Power Polygons** In this unit, students use the Power Polygon pieces to sort and build polygons and to study angle size. The Power Polygons are three-dimensional objects that are used to study two-dimensional shapes by focusing on one of the faces. For this purpose, Power Polygons are called by their 2-D names. For example, Power Polygon piece H (a hexagon) is called a hexagon even though it is a hexagonal prism. Power Polygons (M15) provides an illustration of all the shapes in the Power Polygon set for your reference.

20 MIN   CLASS

DISCUSSION

❶ Regular Polygons

Math Focus Points for Discussion

◆ Defining a regular polygon as a polygon with all sides and all angles equal

Today in Math Workshop, you'll be playing *Guess My Rule* with Power Polygons.❶ You may remember these materials from Grade 4. Take a look at the sets you have in front of you. What can you tell us about these pieces?

Give students a few minutes to re-familiarize themselves with the Power Polygons. They might notice that they include different sizes and types of quadrilaterals and triangles as well as one other polygon (a hexagon). They also might observe that they fit together in a variety of ways and that they are each identified by a letter. Some may recognize the shapes of the Pattern Blocks with which they worked in previous grades, and some may remember that they used these pieces to find the measurement of angles.

Let's start by playing one round of *Guess My Rule* with the Power Polygons together.

In order to have students consider another category of polygons, those that are *regular*, your rule for this round will be "all sides and all angles equal." Place Power Polygon pieces A (square) and I (equilateral triangle) on the overhead.

Find a polygon in your set that you think fits my rule, and talk to your neighbor about why you think it fits.

There are only three other polygons in the set that fit this rule: pieces B, H, and N. These make up the subset of regular polygons in the Power Polygons set. Some students may offer one of the three nonsquare rhombuses in the set (pieces G, M, and O), thinking that the rule is limited to having all equal sides. If this happens, place these separately on the overhead, and tell students that these do not fit your rule. Ask for other examples of polygons that do not fit the rule. Once students have agreed that the rule includes both equal sides and equal angles, let them know that this is a special category of polygons.

The teacher shows that a rhombus is not in the set of regular polygons.

Polygons like these that have all sides equal and all angles equal are called *regular polygons.* In this set we have regular quadrilaterals, which we usually call squares, regular triangles, which are also called equilateral triangles, and a regular hexagon. Let's look at a few more examples of regular polygons.

Display Polygons: Regular and Not Regular (T61) on the overhead. Spend a few minutes discussing the figures at the top of the page. Invite several students to come up and count the sides of the figures besides the triangle and square and ask the class what to call these (regular heptagon, regular octagon, regular pentagon, and regular decagon). Then, choose one or two figures at the bottom of the page to discuss. Ask questions such as these:

Are there any figures here that look like they might be regular, but are not? How can you tell that they're not?

Are there any figures here that have all equal sides but not all equal angles? All equal angles but not all equal sides?

Let students know that in Math Workshop today they will be working on an activity about deciding whether a polygon is regular.

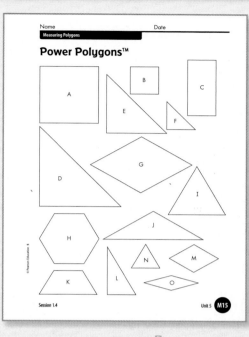

▲ **Resource Masters, M15; T60**

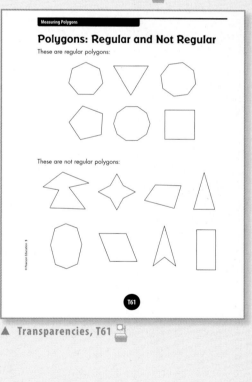

▲ **Transparencies, T61**

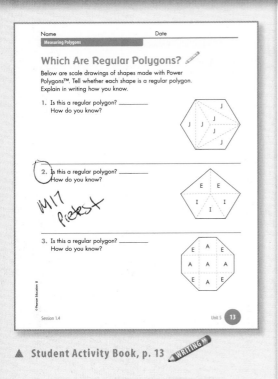

▲ Student Activity Book, p. 13

MATH WORKSHOP

40 MIN

② Working with Power Polygons

In this Math Workshop, students work on two activities that make use of the Power Polygons. In the first activity, Which Are Regular Polygons?, they consider polygons that are constructed from Power Polygons and determine whether they are regular. They also play *Guess My Rule* with Power Polygons. These activities help students become familiar with attributes of the Power Polygon set, including shapes and angles. They will use the set to measure angles more extensively during later sessions in this investigation. Students also continue to develop understanding of supplementary angles through the *LogoPaths Angle and Turn Game*.

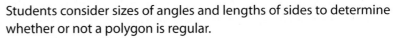

2A Which Are Regular Polygons?

INDIVIDUALS

Have students work on *Student Activity Book* page 13, reminding them that a regular polygon has equal sides and equal angles. Students consider three figures and explain why each is regular or not. They should have Power Polygons on hand as they work on this activity.

ONGOING ASSESSMENT: Observing Students at Work

Students consider sizes of angles and lengths of sides to determine whether or not a polygon is regular.

- **Do students consider both the sizes of the angles and the lengths of the sides to determine whether or not a polygon is regular?**

- **Do students use measurement, either with Power Polygons or in some other way, to verify angle sizes and side lengths, rather than judging by appearance?**

As you observe students working on this activity, keep in mind that it is not necessary for students to determine the exact measurement of each angle in the polygons (which will be the focus of the next three sessions). Fifth graders should be able to use the polygon pieces to compare the sizes of angles to find whether they are the same. You may want to remind students of the work they did with measuring Power Polygon angles in Grade 4. Some may actually remember or be able to reconstruct the angle sizes of some of these particular polygons, but this should not be expected at this point.

DIFFERENTIATION: Supporting the Range of Learners

Intervention For students having difficulty using the different shapes of the Power Polygons to compare angle sizes, suggest that they make a tracing of one of the angles in a polygon they have questions about, and then use that to see whether the other angles are the same size. Students also may use this method to measure side lengths, or they may use rulers.

2B *Guess My Rule* with Power Polygons

GROUPS

Students play *Guess My Rule* using the Power Polygon pieces instead of Shape Cards. For complete details about this activity, see Session 1.3, page 41.

2C *LogoPaths: Angle and Turn Game* (optional)

PAIRS

For complete details about this activity, see Session 1.2, pages 36–38.

SESSION FOLLOW-UP

Daily Practice and Homework

 Daily Practice: For ongoing review, have students complete *Student Activity Book* page 14.

 Homework: Students distinguish between quadrilaterals with one and two sets of parallel sides on *Student Activity Book* page 15.

Student Math Handbook: Students and families may use *Student Math Handbook* pages 93–94 for reference and review. See pages 170–173 in the back of this unit.

Name _____ Date _____

Measuring Polygons

Daily Practice

Fraction and Percent Problems

Solve the following problems. Explain how you determined your answers.

NOTE Students solve problems about fractions and percents of a group.

SMH 40–41

1. Rachel, Olivia, and Deon make their own pizzas. All three pizzas are the same size.
   a. Rachel cut her pizza into four equal pieces and ate three pieces. What fraction of the pizza did she eat?
   b. Olivia cut her pizza into eight equal pieces and ate five pieces. What fraction of the pizza did she eat?
   c. Deon cut his pizza into six equal pieces and ate five pieces. What fraction of pizza did he eat?
   d. Who ate the most pizza? Who ate the least? How do you know?

2. Nora and Zachary made juice smoothies and poured them equally into 2 glasses that are the same size. Nora drank $\frac{2}{3}$ of her smoothie. Zachary drank 75% of his. Who drank more of their smoothie? How do you know?

3. Lourdes ate 25% of a sandwich. Mitch ate 50% of a different sandwich. Mitch claims that he ate the same amount as Lourdes. Explain how this is possible.

14 Unit 5   Session 1.4

▲ **Student Activity Book, p. 14**

Name _____ Date _____

Measuring Polygons

Homework

Parallel or Not?

Parallel lines never meet. Parallel segments or sides are parts of parallel lines.

NOTE Students distinguish between different types of quadrilaterals, focusing on the attribute of parallel sides.

SMH 17

1. Circle the shapes with exactly 1 pair of parallel sides.

2. Circle the shapes with 2 pairs of parallel sides.

3. Draw a shape that has
   • 4 sides in all
   • 2 right angles
   • 1 pair of parallel sides

4. Explain the difference between a parallelogram and a rectangle.

_____

_____

_____

Session 1.4   Unit 5 15

▲ **Student Activity Book, p. 15**

Angle Sizes in Polygons

Math Focus Points

◆ Using known angles to find the measures of other angles

Vocabulary

interior angle

Today's Plan		Materials
ACTIVITY ❶ **Introducing Angles in the Power Polygons**	🕐 20 MIN 👥 CLASS 👥 PAIRS	• Power Polygons; blank transparencies
ACTIVITY ❷ **Angles in the Power Polygons**	🕐 40 MIN 👥 PAIRS	• *Student Activity Book,* pp. 17–19 • Power Polygons
ACTIVITY ❸ **Introducing *LogoPaths* Activities: *Triangles* and *Rhombuses and Parallelograms* (optional)**	👥 CLASS	• Computers with *LogoPaths* software installed
SESSION FOLLOW-UP ❹ **Daily Practice and Homework**		• *Student Activity Book,* pp. 20–21 • *Student Math Handbook,* pp. 99–101

Ten-Minute Math

Quick Images: 2-D Show Images 9 and 10 of *Quick Images: 2-D* (T55) one at a time and follow the procedure for the basic routine. For each image, students discuss how they drew their figures, including any revisions they made after each viewing.

Ask students:

• How did you remember the parts of the image?

• What did you notice about the relationship of the parts of the image?

• What helped you remember the whole image so that you could draw your design?

ACTIVITY

1 Introducing Angles in the Power Polygons

20 MIN   CLASS   PAIRS

Place Power Polygon piece D (isosceles right triangle) on the overhead, and trace the shape on a blank transparency.

Today you're going to be measuring angles in the Power Polygons. What can you tell us about the angles in this polygon?

Students should notice that one of the angles is a right angle, or 90 degrees, and that the other two angles are equal and acute, or smaller than 90°.

If we already know that one of these angles is 90 degrees because it's a right angle, how can you find the exact measures of the other two angles? Work with your partner to find this measure. You may use any of the other Power Polygons to help you.

Give students a few minutes to work on this, and then collect their responses.

Students might say:

"The two smaller angles are the same size, and together they fit on top of the 90° angle. They're half of 90, so that's 45 degrees."

When the class agrees on the angle sizes, mark each angle and write 90° in the right angle and 45° in each of the smaller angles as shown.

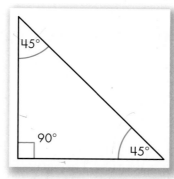

Another way we can prove that the two smaller angles are 45° is to put a number of them around a point.

Draw a dot on the overhead. Take four of triangle D and begin to place them around in a circle with a 45° vertex of each touching the dot. This creates a 180° angle, which forms a straight line.

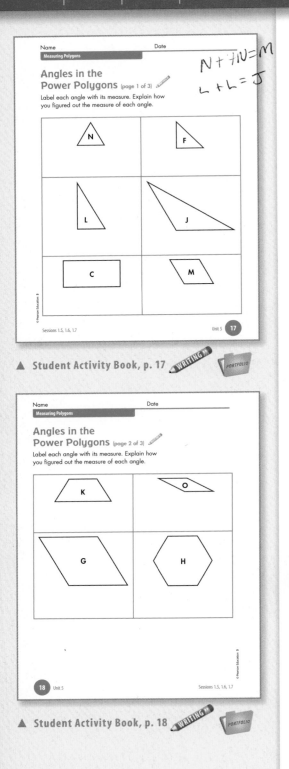

▲ Student Activity Book, p. 17 — WRITING — PORTFOLIO

▲ Student Activity Book, p. 18 — WRITING — PORTFOLIO

handwritten notes:

$N + 7N = M$

$L + L = J$

handwritten: circle thing for 1.6

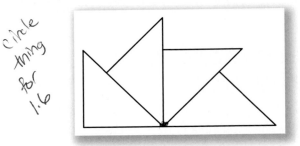

Before I keep going, how many degrees have I filled in so far? . . . In other words, how much is 45° times 4? . . . What does that tell us about the measure of an angle like this, which looks like a straight line?

From their work with *LogoPaths,* students may already be familiar with the idea that angles totaling 180° will form a straight line. They may also reason that two 90° angles, which make a line when fitted together, also sum to 180°.

If I keep adding triangles around this same point, how many triangles in all will I need to go all the way around the point? [8] . . . Can you predict how many degrees that would be? . . . How can knowing it takes 360° to go all the way around help you figure out how many degrees each angle must be?

Add four more copies of triangle D to complete the figure. Give students a few minutes to discuss this method of finding the measures of angles by completing a rotation and considering the angles around the center point as a fraction of 360°. It is likely that not all students will be convinced by this method at the end of this activity.

ACTIVITY

40 MIN   PAIRS

2 Angles in the Power Polygons

Have students work in pairs on *Student Activity Book* pages 17–19. Let students know that they can work on these problems in any order and that what they figure out about one Power Polygon piece can be used for the others.

As students work on finding the angle sizes in the Power Polygons, notice the strategies they use. They may also use the idea that a 180° angle looks like a straight line and a full rotation measures 360°. Students may compare angle sizes to 90° or combine a number of known angles to find the measure of a larger angle.

Students find the measure of one of the smaller angles in Power Polygon piece J by combining them to form a right angle or a straight line.

Name _____ Date _____

Measuring Polygons

Angles in the Power Polygons (page 3 of 3)

Use the information you found about angle measures on pages 17 and 18 to help you answer these questions.

1. Look at Power Polygon N. What is the sum of all three angles in this triangle?

2. If you add up the angles in the other Power Polygon triangles, will you find the same sum? Why or why not? (First write your prediction, and then check to see whether you are right.)

3. Find the sums of the angles in each of the quadrilaterals in the Power Polygons. What do you notice?

4. Look at the sums of the angles in the triangles and compare them to the sums of the angles in the quadrilaterals. What do you notice? Why do you think this is?

Sessions 1.5, 1.6, 1.7   Unit 5   **19**

▲ **Student Activity Book, p. 19** WRITING PORTFOLIO

On *Student Activity Book* page 19, which is optional, students have the opportunity to explore the sum of the angles in polygons and how sums differ depending on the type of polygon. Some students may have already noticed from their work with *LogoPaths* that the interior angles of some triangles (such as equilateral) sum to 180°; in this part of the activity they use the angle measures they found in the Power Polygons to consider whether this is true for all triangles. Students also explore the sums of angles in quadrilaterals and why this might be different than the sums of angles in triangles. It is not expected that all students will do this part of the activity, because students will further explore this idea in later grades.

ONGOING ASSESSMENT: Observing Students at Work

Students find the measures of the angles in Power Polygons, using right angles and other known angle measurements as landmarks.

- **Are students combining known angles to match with the angle they are trying to determine?**

- **Are students writing number relationships that match the angle combinations they have made?**

- **Are students including all of the steps in their reasoning when they write explanations?**

As students work, ask questions to help them focus on how they are using what they already know about some angle measurements to find new ones such as:

- How can you use a 90° angle to help you find the angles in this equilateral triangle? Can you find another angle that will fit with this one to make a right angle? What does that tell you about the size of each of these acute angles?

- Are there any angles that you already know the measure of that you can combine to make this obtuse angle?

- How would it help to compare this angle with a straight line or fit copies of this angle all the way around?

DIFFERENTIATION: Supporting the Range of Learners

Intervention If some students have difficulty combining smaller angles to make angles that match those in the Power Polygon set, modify the activity. These students should instead build new angles by piecing together some of the Power Polygon pieces and then determine the size of the angle that they built. Offer this as an example: three of the Power Polygon pieces L fit together to make a right angle. From this, you can conclude that the smallest angle in L is 30° (90° divided 3). Challenge the students to build angles of 60°, 90°, 120°, and 150° by using one or more of the Power Polygon angles. Have them record what angles they used for each measure. When they return to examining angles in the next session, they can use the angles they built as a guide.

Turtlepaths handout -see

ACTIVITY

CLASS

3 Introducing *LogoPaths* Activities: *Triangles* and *Rhombuses and Parallelograms* (optional)

In these activities, students use *Free Explore* in the *LogoPaths* software to draw triangles, rhombuses, and parallelograms. In this investigation, students draw equilateral triangles of different sizes, focusing on the properties of these triangles—three equal sides and three equal angles. In Investigation 2, students use the *LogoPaths* software to draw rhombuses and parallelograms. As they do so, they deepen their understanding of the properties of these shapes—four equal sides in rhombuses, opposite sides equal in parallelograms, opposite angles equal in both, and adjacent interior angles adding to 180° in both. In addition, all of these activities continue to develop students' understanding of the relationship between the turning angle and the interior angle formed by that turn. ❶

Open *Free Explore* in the *LogoPaths* software and, if necessary, spend a couple of minutes reviewing the forward (**FD**), backward (**BK**), right (**RT**) and left (**LT**) turn commands, and reminding students how to use the Turtle Turner, Ruler, Label Lengths, and Label Turns tools. Then introduce the *Triangles* activity.

Your task in this *LogoPaths* activity is to draw equilateral triangles. What do you need to know about equilateral triangles in order to do this task? [Equilateral triangles have three equal sides and three equal angles] What commands could we use to draw the first side?

Students may suggest moving the turtle forward, using a command such as **FD 100**, to form a side of the triangle pictured below.

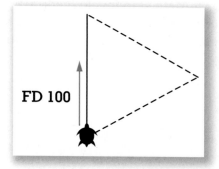

Alternately, they may suggest first turning the turtle 90° before moving it forward, using a command such as **RT 90**, **FD 100**, to form the base of the triangle pictured below. ❷

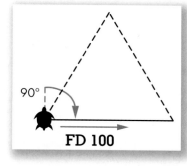

After you've drawn the first side of your triangle, you'll need to turn before you draw the next side. You may have to try a few different turns before you find the turning angle you need for an equilateral triangle. Remember that all three turns must be the same. You can use the Turtle Turner tool to help you figure out what turn to use.

Professional Development

❶ **Teacher Note:** *The Rule of 180°*, p. 142

Teaching Note

❷ **Drawing a side before the horizontal base**
Some students may assume that a triangle needs to have a flat (horizontal) base. Because the turtle begins in a facing upward position, if these students chose to draw a "side" first, they will first need to turn the turtle 30° as shown in the figure below. It may be difficult for students to know the size of turn needed to make this come out right. Encourage them to experiment with different initial turns. Also help them notice that after this first orienting turn, the turn commands needed to make the triangle are the same as for any equilateral triangle.

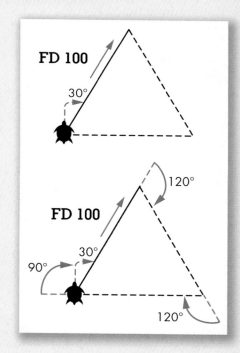

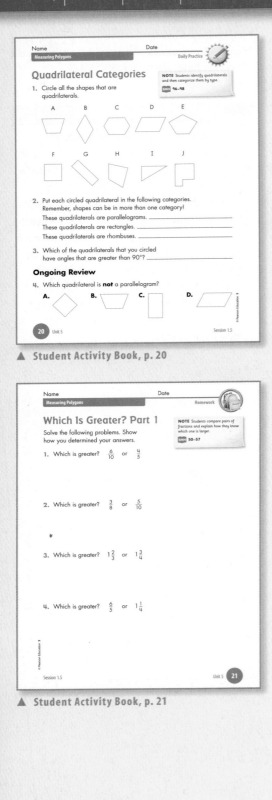

▲ **Student Activity Book, p. 20**

▲ **Student Activity Book, p. 21**

During Math Workshop the next two days, you'll have time to work on the *Triangles* activity. Later, you can use what you've learned drawing triangles and what you know about quadrilaterals to draw rhombuses and parallelograms with the *LogoPaths* software. Just be sure that you work on the *Triangles* activity before you move on to *Rhombuses and Parallelograms*.

SESSION FOLLOW-UP

4 Daily Practice and Homework

Daily Practice: For reinforcement of this unit's content, have students complete *Student Activity Book* page 20.

Homework: On *Student Activity Book* page 21, students compare pairs of fractions and explain how they know which is greater.

Student Math Handbook: Students and families may use *Student Math Handbook* pages 99–101 for reference and review. See pages 170–173 in the back of this unit.

Examining Angles and Classifying Polygons

Math Focus Points

◆ Using known angles to find the measures of other angles

◆ Identifying attributes of polygons

Vocabulary

exterior angle

Today's Plan		Materials
① DISCUSSION **Strategies for Finding Angle Measures**	🕐 20 MIN 👥 CLASS	• Power Polygons
② MATH WORKSHOP **Angles and Polygons** **②A** Angles in the Power Polygons **②B** *Guess My Rule* **②C** *LogoPaths: Triangles* (optional)	🕐 40 MIN	**②A** • *Student Activity Book,* pp. 17–19 (from Session 1.5) • Power Polygons **②B** • Shape Cards (from Session 1.1) **②C** • M1* • Computers with *LogoPaths* software installed
③ SESSION FOLLOW-UP **Daily Practice**		• *Student Activity Book,* p. 23 • *Student Math Handbook,* pp. 93, 95, 96–98, 99–101

*See *Materials to Prepare,* p. 23.

Ten-Minute Math

Quick Images: 2-D Show Images 11 and 12 of *Quick Images: 2-D* (T55) one at a time and follow the procedure for the basic routine. For each image, students discuss how they drew their figures, including any revisions they made after each viewing.

Ask students:

• How did you remember the parts of the image?

• What did you notice about the relationship of the parts of the image?

• What helped you remember the whole image so that you could draw your design?

Professional Development

❶ **Dialogue Box:** *Finding Angle Measures of Power Polygons,* p. 163

DISCUSSION

① Strategies for Finding Angle Measures

20 MIN   CLASS

Math Focus Points For Discussion

◆ Using known angles to find the measure of other angles

Begin this discussion by asking two or three students to explain how they found the angles in Power Polygon piece L. Choose students whose work covers the range of strategies that students have been considering, such as comparing angle sizes to 90 degrees, combining a number of known angles to find the measure of a larger angle, or using knowledge that a 180° angle looks like a straight line and a full rotation measures 360°. When a student presents an explanation, have one student write the numerical steps on the board and another act out the explanation with the Power Polygons on the overhead.❶

As you listen to a classmate present an explanation, act out what your classmate says with your own pieces. Be prepared to restate the explanation in your own words or ask a question if there is a part you do not understand.

For example, students might have several ways of examining the angles in piece L (30–60–90).

Students might say:

"I know the large angle in L is a right angle, because it matched the angle in Shape D. I did the smallest angle next. I pieced together three of them and saw they made a right angle. 90 divided by 3 is 30, and so the smallest angle is 30 degrees. Then I found out that two of the smallest angles fit exactly to make the other acute angle, and so it must be 60 (30 + 30 is 60)."

"I saw the right angle. I could tell because it matched angles in the square A. Then I put together two of the pieces and made a rectangle. I know rectangles have right angles, and so I knew that together these two smaller angles in L made 90 degrees. At first I thought they were 45 degrees, but when I put them on top of each other I saw they were not the same. Then I noticed that two of the little ones fit on the big one and that made me think of 30 and 60. I tried that and it was right."

"I started to do the circle thing with the bigger angle that wasn't 90 degrees. But when I put three together, I already had a straight line, and 180 divided by 3 is 60, so each angle has to be 60°. If you go all the way around it would take 6 angles, but they'd still be 60° because 360 divided by 6 is 60."

Choose one or two more angles to discuss, such as J (isosceles obtuse triangle) or M (nonrectangular rhombus). Keep this discussion to about 20 minutes, so that students have time to use the strategies that come up when they return to the activity in Math Workshop.

MATH WORKSHOP
Angles and Polygons

40 MIN

Have students continue to work on finding the measure of angles in the Power Polygons by finishing *Student Activity Book* pages 17 and 18. They may then choose to complete page 19, play *Guess My Rule,* or work on the *LogoPaths* activity, *Triangles.*

2A Angles in the Power Polygons

PAIRS

For complete details about this activity, see Session 1.5, pages 51–54.

2B *Guess My Rule*

GROUPS

For complete details about this activity, see Session 1.3, page 41.

Teaching Note

❷ **Similar Triangles** When students create equilateral triangles of different sizes, they are beginning to work on the geometric idea of *similarity*. This idea will be explored further in Investigation 3.

Technology Note

❸ **Using the Repeat Command to Draw Equilateral Triangles** The repeat command tells the turtle to repeat a set of commands a specified number of times. The first input is the number of times to repeat, and the second is a list of commands enclosed in square brackets. For example, to draw a triangle with side lengths of 200 turtle steps (perimeter 600), students could enter **REPEAT 3 [FD 200 RT 120]** in the Command Center. This set of commands instructs the turtle to repeat a forward move of 200 and a right turn of 120 three times. To draw a triangle with side lengths of 300 turtle steps (perimeter 900), students could enter **REPEAT 3 [FD 300 RT 120]**. This set of commands instructs the turtle to repeat a forward move of 300 and a right turn of 120 three times.

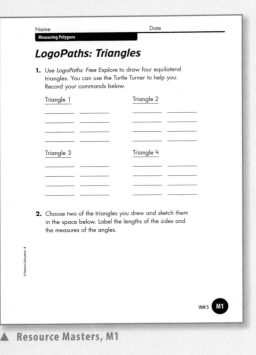

▲ Resource Masters, M1

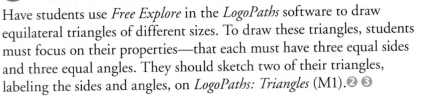

②C LogoPaths: Triangles (optional)

PAIRS

Have students use *Free Explore* in the *LogoPaths* software to draw equilateral triangles of different sizes. To draw these triangles, students must focus on their properties—that each must have three equal sides and three equal angles. They should sketch two of their triangles, labeling the sides and angles, on *LogoPaths: Triangles* (M1).❷ ❸

ONGOING ASSESSMENT: Observing Students at Work

Students use their understanding of the properties of equilateral triangles to draw these shapes with the *LogoPaths* software.

- **Do students use the *LogoPaths* commands fluently?**

- **Do students demonstrate understanding that equilateral triangles have three equal sides and three equal angles?**

- **Are students able to use turns to create interior angles less than 90°?** Do they demonstrate understanding that the greater the turn, the smaller the angle produced?

- **Do students understand that to create a certain interior angle, they must use a turn that is the supplement of that angle?** For example, do they understand that to create an interior angle of 60°, they need to turn the turtle 120°?

- **Have some students noticed that the interior angles add to 180°?**

- **Are students able to correctly label the angles of the triangles they draw?** In other words, do they distinguish the interior angles from the turns or exterior angles?

DIFFERENTIATION: Supporting the Range of Learners

Intervention Some students may have difficulty figuring out how to create interior angles less than 90°. Encourage them to experiment with different turns and to observe the resulting angles. For example:

- I see that you moved forward 100 steps, turned 60°, and then moved forward 100 steps. Can you show me the angle you made between the lines you drew? Is it less than or greater than 90°? If you made a bigger turn, what do you think would happen to the angle? Why don't you try that?

Intervention Some students may have difficulty determining the size of the interior angles needed to create an equilateral triangle. Provide them with an equilateral triangle, such as shape I, from the set of Power Polygons and any Power Polygon with a right angle, such as shape A. Ask questions like:

- Can you use this 90° angle to help you figure out the size of the angles in this triangle? What turn could you use to draw an angle this size?

Extension Students moving easily through this activity can be challenged to draw other types of triangles, such as scalene, isosceles, right, obtuse, or acute. For any of these triangles, it may be easy for students to draw the first two sides and the angle between them. However, they may need to use the Turtle Turner to measure the turning angle back to their starting spot, and the Ruler to measure the distance.

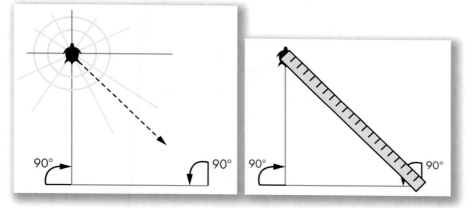

After the students have successfully returned the turtle to its starting spot, encourage them to find the turn needed to get it facing along the first side. They may start to notice that the three turns (exterior angles) always sum to 360°.

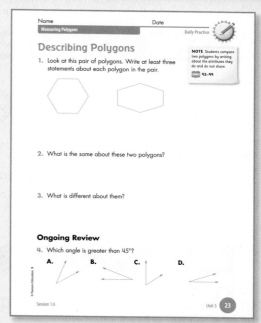

▲ Student Activity Book, p. 23

SESSION FOLLOW-UP
3 Daily Practice

 Daily Practice: For reinforcement of this unit's content, have students complete *Student Activity Book* page 23.

Student Math Handbook: Students and families may use *Student Math Handbook* pages 93, 95, 96–98, and 99–101 for reference and review. See pages 170–173 in the back of this unit.

Assessment: Quadrilaterals and Angles

Math Focus Points

◆ Using attributes to describe and compare quadrilaterals including parallelograms, rectangles, rhombuses, and squares

◆ Using known angles to find the measures of other angles

Today's Plan		Materials
ASSESSMENT ACTIVITY **①** **Assessment: Quadrilaterals and Angles**	✓ ⏱ 30 MIN 👤 INDIVIDUALS	• M17*
MATH WORKSHOP **②** **Angles and Polygons** **2A** Angles in the Power Polygons **2B** *Guess My Rule* **2C** *LogoPaths: Triangles* (optional)	⏱ 30 MIN	**2A** • *Student Activity Book,* pp. 17–19 (from Session 1.5) • Power Polygons **2B** • Shape Cards (from Session 1.1) **2C** • M1 (from Session 1.6) • Computers with *LogoPaths* software installed
SESSION FOLLOW-UP **③** **Daily Practice and Homework**		• *Student Activity Book,* pp. 24–25 • *Student Math Handbook,* pp. 95, 96–98, 99–101

*See *Materials to Prepare,* p. 23.

Ten-Minute Math

Quick Images: 2-D Show Images 13 and 14 of *Quick Images: 2-D* (T56) one at a time and follow the procedure for the basic routine. For each image, students discuss how they drew their figures, including any revisions they made after each viewing.

Ask students:

• How did you remember the parts of the image?

• What did you notice about the relationship of the parts of the image?

• What helped you remember the whole image so that you could draw your design?

1 ASSESSMENT ACTIVITY
Quadrilaterals and Angles

30 MIN INDIVIDUALS

Have students work on Assessment: Quadrilaterals and Angles (M17) in order to assess their work in this Investigation.❶ Let them know that they should work individually on this assignment.❷

ONGOING ASSESSMENT: Observing Students at Work

Students write about the relationships among different types of quadrilaterals and find the measures of the angles in an irregular polygon.

- **Can students express the relationships among parallelograms, rhombuses, and squares?**

- **Can students determine the size of the angles in a polygon by combining other known angles?** Do they add familiar angle sizes to get angle sizes that are less familiar, such as adding 60° and 45° to get 105°?

- **Can students express the steps in their reasoning in a written argument?**

DIFFERENTIATION: Supporting the Range of Learners

Intervention If some students have trouble writing their explanations, have them first explain their thinking out loud to you, and then have them write what they say. Note that these students need ongoing support in recording their thinking for themselves.

2 MATH WORKSHOP
Angles and Polygons

30 MIN

Students who have not yet finished finding the measures of angles in the Power Polygons should continue to work on that activity. Decide which students would benefit from going on to *Student Activity Book* page 19, and which students should continue to play *Guess My Rule* in order to solidify their understanding of the attributes and classification of polygons. Some students may also work on the *LogoPaths* activity, *Triangles*.

Professional Development

❶ This assessment focuses on Benchmarks 1 and 2. Students demonstrate understanding that the same quadrilateral (a square) can be classified in several ways (rhombus and parallelogram), and find angles in a quadrilateral.

❷ **Teacher Note:** Assessment: Quadrilaterals and Angles, p. 143

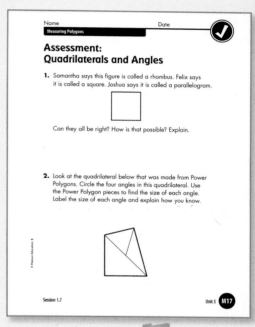

▲ **Resource Masters, M17** PORTFOLIO

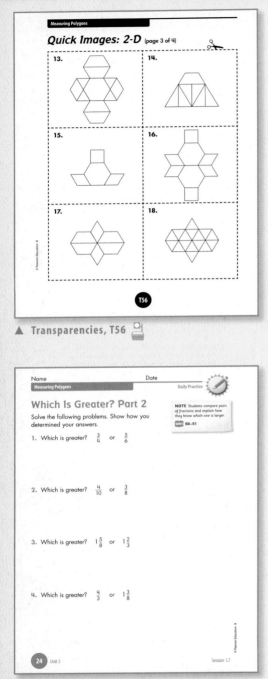

Quick Images: 2-D (page 3 of 4)

13. 14.
15. 16.
17. 18.

T56

▲ Transparencies, T56

Name _____ Date _____

Measuring Polygons   Daily Practice

Which Is Greater? Part 2

Solve the following problems. Show how you determined your answers.

NOTE Students compare pairs of fractions and explain how they know which one is larger.
50–51

1. Which is greater? $\frac{3}{4}$ or $\frac{5}{6}$

2. Which is greater? $\frac{4}{10}$ or $\frac{3}{8}$

3. Which is greater? $1\frac{5}{8}$ or $1\frac{2}{3}$

4. Which is greater? $\frac{4}{3}$ or $1\frac{3}{8}$

24 Unit 5   Session 1.7

▲ Student Activity Book, p. 24

2A Angles in the Power Polygons

PAIRS

For complete details about this activity, see Session 1.5, pages 51–54.

2B *Guess My Rule*

GROUPS

For complete details about this activity, see Session 1.3, page 41.

2C *LogoPaths: Triangles* (optional)

PAIRS

For complete details about this activity, see Session 1.6, pages 60–61.

SESSION FOLLOW-UP

3 Daily Practice and Homework

Daily Practice: For ongoing review, have students complete *Student Activity Book* page 24.

Homework: On *Student Activity Book* page 25, students identify polygons based on descriptions of their attributes.

Student Math Handbook: Students and families may use *Student Math Handbook* pages 95, 96–98, and 99–101 for reference and review. See pages 170–173 in the back of this unit.

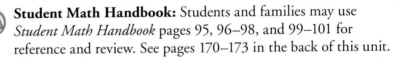

Name _____ Date _____

Measuring Polygons   Homework

Follow the Rules

Circle the shape that follows each set of rules.

NOTE Students practice identifying properties of polygons.
43

1. • It has 3 sides.
   • It has 1 right angle.
   • It has 2 sides the same length.

2. • It has exactly one pair of parallel sides.
   • No 2 of the angles are the same size.

3. • It has fewer than 4 sides.
   • It has 1 obtuse angle.
   • It has 2 angles that are the same size.

4. • It has 5 sides.
   • It has 2 right angles.
   • It has exactly 1 pair of parallel sides.

5. • It has exactly 2 pairs of parallel sides.
   • It has 0 right angles.
   • The sides are not all the same length.

Ongoing Review

6. Crystal ran 9.6 miles each week. How many miles did she run in two weeks?
   A. 4.8 mi   **B.** 18.12 mi   **C.** 18.2 mi   **D.** 19.2 mi

Session 1.7   Unit 5 25

▲ Student Activity Book, p. 25

Mathematical Emphasis

Linear and Area Measurement Finding perimeter and area

Math Focus Points

◆ Comparing the perimeters and areas of rectangles when the dimensions are multiplied by given amounts

◆ Using numerical and/or geometric patterns to describe how the perimeters and areas of rectangles change when the dimensions change

◆ Using representations to explain how perimeters and areas of rectangles change

◆ Creating different rectangles with the same area but different perimeters

◆ Understanding square units as a unit of measure

◆ Creating different rectangles with the same perimeter but different areas

◆ Describing the shapes of rectangles that have the same area or the same perimeter

Finding Perimeter and Area of Related Rectangles

	Student Activity Book	Student Math Handbook	Professional Development: Read Ahead of Time	
SESSION 2.1 p. 70				
A Sequence of Squares Students find the perimeter and area of a series of related squares. They consider how a change in the dimensions of a square changes the perimeter and the area.	27–29	102	• **Part 4: Ten-Minute Math** in *Implementing Investigations in Grade 5: Quick Survey*	
SESSION 2.2 p. 76				
Doubling Dimensions of Squares Students use representations to explain how the areas and perimeters of squares change when the dimensions are doubled. In an optional activity that builds on Investigation 1 work with polygons and the measurement of angles, students use *LogoPaths* software to draw rhombuses and parallelograms.	27, 31–34	102	• **Dialogue Box:** Doubling the Dimensions, p. 165	
SESSION 2.3 p. 83				
Building a Sequence of Rectangles Students work with rectangles that are not squares as they continue to examine how changing the dimensions of a rectangle changes the perimeter and area.	35–38	102		
SESSION 2.4 p. 89				
Different Perimeter, Same Area Students "rearrange" rectangles to find several rectangles with different perimeters but the same area.	39–41	102		
SESSION 2.5 p. 95				
Measuring Rectangles Students begin a Math Workshop focusing on finding and comparing the areas and perimeters of rectangles. They build or draw rectangles that all have the same perimeter and rectangles that have the same area. They continue using the *LogoPaths* software to draw rhombuses and parallelograms.	43–45	102		

Ten-Minute Math See page 16 for an overview.

Quick Images: 2-D
- T56, *Quick Images: 2-D* 🖳 Set aside images 15–18 for this Investigation.

Quick Survey
- **No materials needed**

Materials to Gather	Materials to Prepare
• **Square tiles** (as needed)	• **M18, Centimeter Grid Paper** Make three copies per student to have available for student use throughout the Investigation. Make additional copies as needed. • **Chart paper** Label the chart paper "Observations About Perimeter and Area."
• **M18, Centimeter Grid Paper** (as needed)	• **M2–M3, *LogoPaths: Rhombuses and Parallelograms*** Make copies. (1 per student; optional) • **Computers with *LogoPaths* software installed** (1 per pair; optional)
• **M18, Centimeter Grid Paper** (1 per student) • **Square tiles** (as needed)	
• **M18, Centimeter Grid Paper** (as needed) • **Square tiles** (24 per student)	
• **M18, Centimeter Grid Paper** (as needed) • **Square tiles** (as needed) • **M2–M3, *LogoPaths: Rhombuses and Parallelograms*** (from Session 2.2)	• **Computers with *LogoPaths* software installed** (1 per pair; optional)

🖳 Overhead Transparency

Finding Perimeter and Area of Related Rectangles, *continued*

SESSION 2.6 p. 100	Student Activity Book	Student Math Handbook	Professional Development: Read Ahead of Time	
Assessment: Perimeter and Area of Rectangles Students continue the Math Workshop on measuring rectangles. They compare rectangles where the perimeter remains the same, and rectangles where the area remains the same. They are assessed on their understanding of perimeter and area.	43–44, 46–47	102	• **Teacher Note:** Assessment: Perimeter and Area of Rectangles, p. 149	

Materials to Gather	Materials to Prepare
• **M18, Centimeter Grid Paper** (as needed) • **Square tiles** (as needed) • **M2–M3,** *LogoPaths: Rhombuses and Parallelograms* (from Session 2.2)	• **M19, Assessment: Perimeter and Area of Rectangles** Make copies. (1 per student) • **Computers with** *LogoPaths* **software installed** (1 per pair; optional)

A Sequence of Squares

Math Focus Points

- Comparing the perimeters and areas of rectangles when the dimensions are multiplied by given amounts

- Using numerical and/or geometric patterns to describe how the perimeters and areas of rectangles change when the dimensions change

Vocabulary

perimeter
area
dimension

Today's Plan		Materials
ACTIVITY **① Introducing** *Quick Survey*	10 MIN CLASS	
ACTIVITY **② Building a Sequence of Squares**	30 MIN PAIRS	• *Student Activity Book,* p. 27 • Squares tiles (as needed)
DISCUSSION **③ Observations About Perimeter and Area**	20 MIN CLASS	• *Student Activity Book,* p. 27 • Chart: Observations About Perimeter and Area*
SESSION FOLLOW-UP **④ Daily Practice and Homework**		• *Student Activity Book,* pp. 28–29 • *Student Math Handbook,* p. 102

*See *Materials to Prepare,* p. 67.

Ten-Minute Math

NOTE: The Ten-Minute Math activity for this unit, *Quick Survey,* is introduced in this session. Plan to do today's Ten-Minute Math sometime after math class, or if it is not possible, choose a Ten-Minute Math activity from a previous unit, such as *Estimation and Number Sense,* with which your students are familiar.

Quick Survey For the survey, ask the class "What is your favorite sport to play?" or a different categorical question that you or the students choose. Make sure they collect data about something they already know or can observe easily. With today's data, make a bar graph. Ask students:

- What do you notice about the data?
- What do the data tell us about our class?

ACTIVITY

① Introducing *Quick Survey*

10 MIN   CLASS

Quick Survey is a new Ten-Minute Math routine that will be used throughout the rest of this unit. Introduce this routine by first drawing a line plot on the board.

* No Time, Don't Do it

We are going to do a new Ten-Minute Math activity today called *Quick Survey*. You may remember this from Grade 4. Today, the question is, "How many buttons are you wearing?" Record your information on the line plot on the board.

A typical line plot for this data looks something like this:

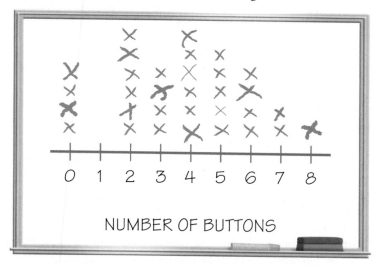

Once data is collected, ask students to describe the data. If they seem uncertain how to do this, ask questions such as:

Are the data spread out or close together?

What is the range (the difference between the lowest and highest values) of the data?

Where does most of the data seem to fall?

What seems typical or usual for the class?

Ask students to interpret the data and predict alternative results by asking a few questions such as:

Why do you think the data came out this way? Did anything surprise you?

Do you think we'd get similar data if we collected it tomorrow, or next week?

Math Notes

❶ Is there a relationship between area and perimeter? In the activities in this Investigation, students work with various collections of rectangles to find both the area and the perimeter of each rectangle in the collection. In Sessions 2.1–2.3, students double the dimensions of rectangles, resulting in a change of both perimeter and area. In Session 2.4, students cut and rearrange rectangles, resulting in rectangles whose areas remain the same, while the perimeters change. In Session 2.5, students find the areas of rectangles that have the same perimeter. One goal of all of these activities is to help students note the differences between these two measures and to see that no simple relationship links them. In order to highlight the differences, the focus of the activities is on the area and perimeter of different rectangles, rather than on the computation of area and perimeter using the dimensions of a particular rectangle.

❷ Using 3-D objects to discuss 1-D and 2-D measurements In this Investigation, students use square tiles, which are in fact 3-dimensional solids, to investigate relationships between the dimensions of a shape and its perimeter and area. The square faces of these tiles are used to represent 2-dimensional figures. Similarly, in Investigation 3, students focus on one face of the Power Polygon pieces to examine perimeter and area.

Would it be different if we did it with a kindergarten class? Or with adults?

The purpose of this activity is to remind students of aspects of data they explored in Grade 4. Their observations and conclusions become more developed and detailed as they continue to examine data throughout this unit. They explore data more fully in *How Long Can You Stand on One Foot?* at the end of the school year.

ACTIVITY

② Building a Sequence of Squares

30 MIN   PAIRS

Begin this activity by reviewing perimeter and area.❶ Hold up one of the square tiles, point to one of its square faces, and describe it as a square with a side length of one inch.❷ Ask students to talk with a partner and figure out the perimeter and area of one square face of the tile.

Focus the conversation on the units of measure by asking questions such as:

How can one tile be both 1 and 4? What are you measuring when you say the perimeter is 4 inches? What are you measuring when you say the area is 1 square inch?

Students should know that perimeter is the distance around a shape—in this case four inches. They should also know that area is the amount of space the object covers—in this case one square inch. Have students turn to *Student Activity Book* page 27 and record the perimeter and area. Remind them that perimeter is measured in linear units, in this case in inches, and area is measured in square units, in this case square inches.

Your task today is to work with a partner to build the squares shown in your Student Activity Book and to record their perimeter and area. While you're working, think about the patterns you are observing. These might be patterns you notice as you're building the squares, or they might be something you notice about the numbers as you record the measurements.

Some students may quickly see and extend the patterns emerging on the chart. Encourage these students to build the squares anyway, both to check their answers and to physically see the changes in perimeter and area.

After students have worked for 20 minutes or so, tell them to answer Question 2 even if they have not completed the chart. Ask them to be prepared to share their observations.

ONGOING ASSESSMENT: Observing Students at Work

Students examine the relationship between the dimensions, area, and perimeter of a series of squares.

- **How are students determining the perimeter of the squares?** Are they counting the tiles on each side, or are they using more than one unit at a time (e.g., skip counting, or multiplying the length of one side times four)?

- **How are students determining the area of the squares?** Are they counting each tile, or are they using more than one unit at a time (e.g., skip counting by rows or columns, or multiplying the two dimensions)?

- **Do students notice patterns in the growth of the area and perimeter of each square?**

- **Do they notice patterns in the way the numbers increase as they build the squares?**

- **Are they recording the perimeter in inches and the area in square inches?**

As you circulate, help students identify patterns by asking questions such as:

- How much is the perimeter increasing each time?

- How much is the area increasing each time?

- Do you notice any patterns in how the area and perimeter grow? Why do you think these patterns appear?

- Can you predict what the perimeter (or area) of the next square is going to be?

DIFFERENTIATION: Supporting the Range of Learners

Intervention Students who are counting by ones (the edges of the square tiles for perimeter, or the number of square faces of each tile for area) should be encouraged to count more efficiently. Once they have counted one side or row or column, ask them how they can use that information to find the perimeter or area more efficiently.

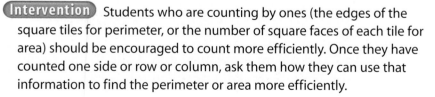

Name _____ Date _____

Measuring Polygons

Building a Sequence of Squares ✏️

1. Use square tiles to build squares of different sizes. Find the perimeter and area of each square. If you have enough time, make additional squares, and write their measurements in the blanks.

Dimensions of Square	Perimeter	Area
1 inch by 1 inch	4	2
2 inches by 2 inches	8	4
3 inches by 3 inches	12	9
4 inches by 4 inches	16	16
5 inches by 5 inches	20	25
6 inches by 6 inches	24	36
7 inches by 7 inches	28	49

2. What patterns do you see? Make a list of observations about the squares, about their perimeters, or about their areas. Write your observations below. Use a separate sheet of paper if necessary.

Sessions 2.1, 2.2   Unit 5   27

▲ Student Activity Book, p. 27

Teaching Note

❸ Finding Perimeter and Area From work in Grades 3 and 4, most fifth graders know how to find the perimeter and area of rectangles. If you find this is not the case with your students, spend a few minutes at the beginning of this discussion reviewing different ways that students are finding these two measurements. Strategies students often use to find perimeter include adding the dimensions together and multiplying by 2 (or in the case of squares, multiplying one length by 4), or by adding each side length. Strategies students often use to find area include multiplying the dimensions, or skip counting the number of tiles or squares on the grid by row or column.

Extension Students who easily fill out the chart should be challenged to predict perimeter and area for larger squares, such as 25 by 25, 50 by 50, 100 by 100. They record their predictions in the blank spaces on *Student Activity Book* page 27.

DISCUSSION

3 Observations About Perimeter and Area

20 MIN   CLASS

Math Focus Points for Discussion

◆ Using numerical and/or geometric patterns to describe how the perimeters and areas of rectangles change when the dimensions change

Post the chart, "Observations About Perimeter and Area," and ask students to share their observations.❸ As each observation is shared, ask:

Does everyone agree that this is true? Who has questions? Who else wrote this as one of their observations?

Once the class has agreed that the observation is true, write it on the chart. While there are many possible observations for this situation, students are likely to notice some of the ideas shown on this chart from one classroom:

> ### Observations About Perimeter and Area
>
> - Squares with odd sides have odd numbers for the area.
> - The numbers for perimeter are all even.
> - The perimeter goes up by 4 each time.
> - The area goes up by odd numbers (first add 3, then add 5, then add 7, etc.).
> - If the sides of the square are doubled so is the perimeter.
> - Each square has the same number of rows and columns.
> - You add a row, a column, and a tile in the corner each time to make a new square.

Choose one of the statements, and ask students to look at their work and to find an explanation for why the statement is true. For example,

Several of you said that when the dimensions of the square increase by one on each side, the perimeter of the square goes up by four inches. Why do you think that is true?

Give students a few minutes to work in pairs, and then bring the students back together to share their ideas. At this point, students are not expected to prove the statements beyond any doubt; however, they should begin to consider why the squares and measurements grow the way they do. Later in this investigation, students examine why some of these patterns exist. End the discussion by asking students to consider several questions.

Here are some questions to think about. Why do you think the perimeter and area change in this way? Do you think this will be true for all squares? We are not going to answer these questions today, but you can begin to think about them.

SESSION FOLLOW-UP

4 Daily Practice and Homework

 Daily Practice: For ongoing review, have students complete *Student Activity Book* page 28.

 Homework: Students decide whether statements comparing fractions and percents of different numbers are true or not true in the *Student Activity Book* page 29.

 Student Math Handbook: Students and families may use *Student Math Handbook* page 102 for reference and review. See pages 170–173 in the back of this unit.

Name _____ Date _____
Measuring Polygons   Daily Practice

Area and Perimeter Fractions and Percents

NOTE Students solve fraction and percent problems involving perimeter and area.
SMH 40–41, 102

Solve the following problems. Show or explain how you determined your answers.

The students in Ms. Jackson's class built rectangles with color tiles.

1. Felix built a 4 inch by 8 inch rectangle.
   a. What is the perimeter of Felix's rectangle? _____
   b. The perimeter of Hana's rectangle is $\frac{2}{3}$ as long as the perimeter of Felix's. What is the perimeter of Hana's rectangle? _____
   c. What is the area of Felix's rectangle? _____
   d. The area of Martin's rectangle is 25% of the area of Felix's. What is the area of Martin's rectangle? _____

Ongoing Review

2. What do you notice about the area of the rectangles below?

   Which rectangle has the longest perimeter?

   A.   B.

   C.

28 Unit 5   Session 2.1

▲ **Student Activity Book, p. 28**

Name _____ Date _____
Measuring Polygons   Homework

True or False?

NOTE Students compare fractions and percents of different numbers.
SMH 48–49, 50–51

Decide whether these statements are true or false. Circle TRUE or FALSE. Explain your reasoning.

Remember, > means greater than.   Example: 3 > 2
         < means less than.   Example: 2 < 3

1. $\frac{3}{4}$ of 80 > $\frac{2}{3}$ of 120   TRUE   FALSE

2. $\frac{1}{4}$ of 36 = $\frac{1}{2}$ of 18   TRUE   FALSE

3. 75% of 200 < 75% of 260   TRUE   FALSE

Session 2.1   Unit 5 29

▲ **Student Activity Book, p. 29** WRITING

Doubling Dimensions of Squares

Math Focus Points

◆ Comparing the perimeters and areas of rectangles when the dimensions are multiplied by given amounts

◆ Using representations to explain how perimeters and areas of rectangles change

Today's Plan		Materials
MATH WORKSHOP **1** **Doubling Area and Perimeter** **1A** Doubling Squares **1B** *LogoPaths: Rhombuses and Parallelograms* (optional)	45 MIN	**1A** • *Student Activity Book,* p. 27 (from Session 2.1); pp. 31–32 • M18 **1B** • M2–M3 • Computers with *LogoPaths* software installed
DISCUSSION **2** **What Doubles?**	15 MIN CLASS	• *Student Activity Book,* pp. 31–32
SESSION FOLLOW-UP **3** **Daily Practice and Homework**		• *Student Activity Book,* pp. 33–34 • *Student Math Handbook,* p. 102

Ten-Minute Math

Quick Survey   For the survey, ask the class "How many books have you read in the last 30 days?" or a different numerical question that you or the students choose. Make sure they collect data about something they already know or can observe easily. With today's data, make a line plot. Ask students:

• What do you notice about the data?

• What do the data tell us about our class?

MATH WORKSHOP

Doubling Area and Perimeter

45 MIN

In the last session, students created a sequence of squares and discussed how changing the dimensions of the square changed the area and perimeter. In one activity in this math workshop, students will consider how and why the perimeter and area change in squares where the dimensions have *doubled.* ❶

In the last session, you made some observations about how changing the dimensions of the square changed both the perimeter and area. In the Math Workshop today, you are going to compare the perimeter and area of squares whose dimensions have been doubled. If we start with the two inch square, which square has dimensions that are doubled? (four inch) What about if we start with the three inch square? (six inch) You'll be looking at those four squares to think about perimeter and area.

For part of the Math Workshop, students may work on the *LogoPaths* activity *Rhombuses and Parallelograms,* using the same procedures as those for the *LogoPaths* activity *Triangles.*

· ·

❶A Doubling Squares

PAIRS

Students use their work on *Student Activity Book* page 27 from the previous session to examine what happens to the perimeter and area when a square's side lengths are doubled. They work on explaining these relationships—why the perimeter of the larger square is doubled and the area of the larger square is four times that of the smaller.

Have students work in pairs on *Student Activity Book* pages 31–32. Remind them to use the square tiles or grid paper drawings of the sequence of squares as they work, and to be ready to share their explanations with the class at the end of the session.

❶ **English Language Learners** To clarify the meaning of the term *doubling* for English Language Learners, you can present a simple situation. [Shandra] has one pencil. If [Renaldo] gives [her] another pencil, [she] now has *double* the number of pencils. How many pencils does [Shandra] have? *(two)* If we *double* the number of pencils again, how many pencils will [she] have? *(four)* So when we *double* an amount, we end up with twice, or *two times,* as much. **Then explain that in this session students will be doubling the lengths and areas of squares.** This square's sides are three inches. If I *double* the length of these sides, how many inches will the new sides be? *(six)*

Name _____ Date _____

Measuring Polygons

Doubling Squares (page 1 of 2) ✏

Use your answers on page 27, *Building a Sequence of Squares,* to answer these questions about how the area of the squares changes.

Record the areas of the following squares:

1. Area of 2-inch square _____

   Area of 4-inch square _____

2. Area of 3-inch square _____

   Area of 6-inch square _____

3. When you double the sides of the square, how does the area of the larger square change?

4. Why does the area change in this way? Use drawings or other representations to show why this change occurs and explain your thinking.

© Pearson Education 3

Session 2.2   Unit 5 **31**

▲ **Student Activity Book, pp. 31–32** WRITING

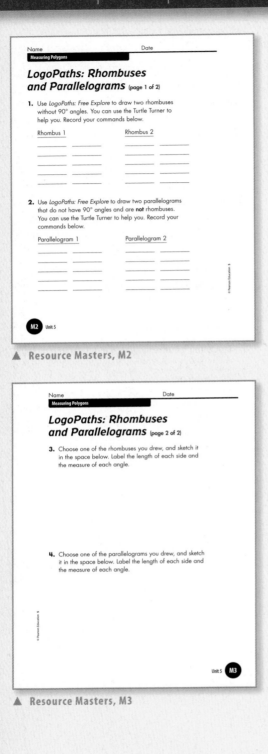

▲ Resource Masters, M2

▲ Resource Masters, M3

Students use different representations to prepare their explanations.

ONGOING ASSESSMENT: Observing Students at Work

Students explain why the perimeter doubles and the area quadruples when the sides of a square are doubled.

- **Do students see the relationship between the perimeters and areas of the squares when the sides are doubled?** (The perimeter doubles and the area quadruples.)

- **What representations do students use to explain how the perimeter and area change when the sides are doubled?** Do they use a numerical approach? (e.g., Area of the larger square increases by four times the smaller in both the two-inch and three-inch squares.) Do they use representations such as a drawing or a model of the squares built with square tiles? (e.g., Even though four times the number of square tiles are used, some sides of tiles are not part of the perimeter because they are "inside" the square.)

DIFFERENTIATION: Supporting the Range of Learners

Intervention For students having difficulty, suggest that they draw a pair of squares on grid paper and work with those two drawings, instead of examining the list of squares on *Student Activity Book* page 27.

Extension For students needing an additional challenge, ask them to consider what happens to the perimeters and areas of squares when the side lengths are tripled.

①B *LogoPaths: Rhombuses and Parallelograms* (optional)

INDIVIDUALS   **PAIRS**

Students use Free Explore in the *LogoPaths* software to draw rhombuses and parallelograms working either alone or with a partner. Have them record the commands used, and draw and label one of each figure on *LogoPaths: Rhombuses and Parallelograms* (M2–M3).❷

ONGOING ASSESSMENT: Observing Students at Work ✓

Students use their understanding of the properties of rhombuses and parallelograms to draw these shapes with the *LogoPaths* software.

- **Do students demonstrate understanding that rhombuses have four equal sides?**

- **Do they demonstrate understanding that opposite sides are equal in parallelograms?**

- **Are students able to use turns to create interior angles greater than and less than 90°?** Do they demonstrate understanding that the greater the turn, the smaller the angle, and vice versa?

- **Do students understand that to create a certain interior angle they must use a turn that is the supplement of that angle?** For example, do they understand that to create an interior angle of 60°, they need to turn the turtle 120°?

- **Do they demonstrate understanding that opposite angles are equal in rhombuses and parallelograms?**

- **Have some students noticed that adjacent interior angles add to 180° in parallelograms (and rhombuses), as do adjacent turning angles?**

Technology Note

❷ **Variable Inputs for Parallelograms**   Each new parallelogram procedure differs from previous parallelogram procedures only in the specific lengths of the sides and the turning angles. Teach students how to use variables in *LogoPaths* by demonstrating the use of variables to write a procedure for parallelograms. Since all parallelograms have two sets of opposite equal sides and consecutive angles that sum to 180°, students may think they need variables for two side lengths and two angles—although they will have to input values for the angles that total 180°.

Step 1: *Define a new procedure*
Begin a new procedure by typing **"to"** and the procedure name on a new line in the Teach window. For example: **to PARALLELOGRAM**

Step 2: *Define the variables*
Just after the procedure name on the same line, name the variables preceded by colons (:). For example: **:SIDE1 :SIDE2 :ANGLE1 :ANGLE2**. (The colon is pronounced "dots").

Step 3: *Define the procedure*
A procedure for a parallelogram can be defined with eleven inputs as shown below:

```
to parallelogram
:side1 :side2 :angle1 :angle2
FD :side1
RT :angle1
FD :side2
RT :angle2
FD :side1
RT :angle1
FD :side2
RT :angle2
end
```

Step 4: *Use the procedure to draw parallelograms*
To use this procedure, type **PARALLELOGRAM** and the side lengths and angle sizes in the Command Center. For example: **PARALLELOGRAM 100 200 50 130**

(Continued on page 80)

Entering these commands will result in a parallelogram with a short side of 100 and a long side of 200 turtle steps with external angles of 50 and 130 degrees.

If the angles do not sum to 180, then the figure will not be a parallelogram. Students can modify the procedure to take only one angle input and use it to calculate the size of the second angle. For example, they might type **"FD :SIDE2 RT (180 − :ANGLE1)"** as part of their procedure.

DIFFERENTIATION: Supporting the Range of Learners

Intervention Some students may have difficulty determining the size of the interior angles, and therefore the turns, needed to create rhombuses and parallelograms. Provide these students with a parallelogram or rhombus (G or M) from the set of Power Polygons and with any Power Polygon with a right angle.

Ask questions such as:

How can you use this 90° angle to help you figure out the size of the angles in this rhombus [parallelogram]? What turns can you use to draw angles that size?

Students may use the angles of the Power Polygons to help them determine angle sizes as they work with LogoPaths.

DISCUSSION
2 What Doubles?

15 MIN   CLASS

Math Focus Points for Discussion

◆ Comparing the perimeters and areas of rectangles when the dimensions are multiplied by given amounts

◆ Using representations to explain how perimeters and areas of rectangles change

Begin the discussion by asking students to share their explanations for what happens to the area of a square when its sides are doubled. ❸

What did you notice about the area of a square when the side lengths are doubled? Why do you think this happens?

Students are expected to notice that when the sides of a square are doubled, the larger square has four times the area of the original square.

Some students might offer numerical arguments, while others might offer arguments based on the diagrams of the square tiles.

Students might say:

"The area of a 2-inch square is 4 square inches, and the area of a 4-inch square is 16 square inches—that's 4 times as much."

"The 3-inch square has 9 tiles, and you need to repeat it 4 times to make a 6-inch square— the 6-inch square has 36 tiles in it. That's 9 times 4."

When different arguments are presented, help students make connections between the math expressions or equations and the various models or representations by asking questions such as:

Some of you used equations to explain the changes, and some of you used drawings of the squares. How are the drawings people made connected to the equations? In the drawings, how do you see that the area is four times larger?

Once students have explained area relationships, ask about perimeter.

What happens to the perimeter of a square when the side lengths are doubled? Why do you think that happens?

Again, some students might offer numerical arguments (the perimeter doubles) and some might offer arguments based on diagrams or the squares built with tiles (showing that not every edge of the square tile becomes part of the perimeter of the larger square).

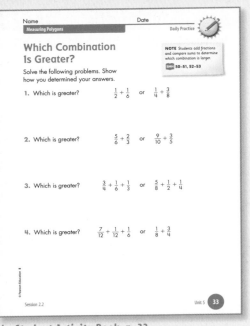

▲ Student Activity Book, p. 33

▲ Student Activity Book, p. 34

Help students connect how a numerical expression matches the corresponding diagram.

So you said that the perimeter doubles every time you double the length of the sides. Can you show me that in these square tiles? What is getting bigger? How much bigger?

Summarize student findings.

So what you're saying is that when we double the length of each side of the square, the perimeter doubles and the area quadruples.

SESSION FOLLOW-UP

3 Daily Practice and Homework

Daily Practice: For ongoing review, have students complete *Student Activity Book* page 33.

Homework: Students determine what categories different triangles and quadrilaterals fit into on *Student Activity Book* page 34.

Student Math Handbook: Student and families may use *Student Math Handbook* page 102 for reference and review. See pages 170–173 in the back of this unit.

Building a Sequence of Rectangles

Math Focus Points

◆ Comparing the perimeters and areas of rectangles when the dimensions are multiplied by given amounts

Today's Plan		Materials
ACTIVITY **① A Sequence of Rectangles**	45 MIN INDIVIDUALS PAIRS	• *Student Activity Book*, pp. 35–36 • M18 • Square tiles
DISCUSSION **② Comparing Rectangles and Squares**	15 MIN CLASS	• *Student Activity Book*, pp. 35–36
SESSION FOLLOW-UP **③ Daily Practice and Homework**		• *Student Activity Book*, pp. 37–38 • *Student Math Handbook*, p. 102

Ten-Minute Math

Quick Images: 2-D Show Images 15 and 16 of *Quick Images: 2-D* (T56) one at a time and follow the procedure for the basic routine. For each image, students discuss how they drew their figures, including any revisions they made after each viewing.

Ask students:

• How did you remember the parts of the image?

• What did you notice about the relationship of the parts of the image?

• What helped you remember the whole image so that you could draw your design?

Just use square tiles on desk

Teaching Note

❶ **3 by 4 and 4 by 3 Rectangles Are the Same** In the following sessions, students begin working with rectangles that are not squares. Sometimes, students consider 3 by 4 and 4 by 3 rectangles as different rectangles. If this issue comes up, let students know that the orientation of the rectangles does not make a difference, because the perimeter and area remain the same.

Name _____ Date _____

Measuring Polygons

A Sequence of Rectangles (page 1 of 2)

Build or draw the sequence of rectangles shown in the table below. Record the perimeter and area for each one. Note that each increase refers to the original rectangle. For example, you should build or draw shape 4 so that its sides are the sides of the original rectangle (3-inch x 4-inch) increased 4 times.

	Dimensions of Rectangle	Perimeter	Area
1. Original	3 inches x 4 inches		
2. All sides x 2			
3. All sides x 3			
4. All sides x 4			
5. All sides x 5			
6. All sides x 6			

7. Imagine a rectangle that has all sides x 10. Predict the following measurements.

Dimensions: _____ Perimeter: _____ Area: _____

Explain your thinking.

© Pearson Education 5

Session 2.3   Unit 5   **35**

▲ **Student Activity Book, p. 35** *WRITING* PORTFOLIO

ACTIVITY

1 A Sequence of Rectangles

45 MIN INDIVIDUALS PAIRS

In the first two sessions, students increased the dimensions of squares to examine how perimeter and area change. In this session, they do the same activity, using rectangles that are not squares.❶

You have been working with squares to think about how perimeter and area change when the sides are increased. Today you are going to do a similar activity, only you are going to use rectangles that are not squares. Do you think the measurements—the dimensions, the perimeter, and the area—will change in the same way as they did with squares? Why?

Briefly solicit a few student ideas.

Have students complete *Student Activity Book* pages 35–36. They may work alone or with a partner, sharing square tiles as needed. Students should draw the larger rectangles (either on blank paper or grid paper) rather than build them with the square tiles. If necessary, remind students of how they drew and labeled arrays in *Number Puzzles* and *Multiple Towers.*

Building the smaller rectangles may help students get started. However, they need to draw larger rectangles since they become too large to build with a limited number of tiles.

Remind students that the change for each new rectangle refers to the original rectangle (e.g., "all sides × 4" means multiply the dimensions of the original 3 inch by 4 inch rectangle by 4).

As students work, they are likely to notice the perimeter of each rectangle increases by 14 (similar to the way the perimeter of each square in Session 2.1 increased by 4). They are not as likely to notice that the change in area is the same as with the squares; it is the original area (12 square inches) times 4, times 9, times 16, and so on.

ONGOING ASSESSMENT: Observing Students at Work

Students examine the relationship between the dimensions, area, and perimeter of a series of rectangles.

- **Do students accurately find the perimeter and area of each rectangle?**

- **Are students able to accurately predict the perimeter and area of the tenth rectangle?** How do they explain their thinking?

- **Do students recognize that as the dimensions are multiplied by given amounts, that the perimeter and area are changing in the rectangles in the same way as the squares?**

As students are working, help them focus on how the perimeter and area are changing, by asking questions such as:

- What do you notice about how the perimeter is changing? Why do you think it is 14 inches each time?

- What do you notice about how the area is changing? How many times larger is the area of the new rectangle than the original? (e.g., For the rectangle whose dimensions are three times larger, how many times larger is the area of 108 square inches than 12 square inches?)

- Can you predict what the perimeter and area of the next rectangle will be without building or drawing it? What about the tenth rectangle?

- Is the same thing happening with these rectangles as happened with the squares? Why do you think that is?

DIFFERENTIATION: Supporting the Range of Learners

Intervention Finding the area of these rectangles provides students with practice in solving multidigit multiplication problems. Students who are still improving their multiplication skills should be allowed to use calculators.

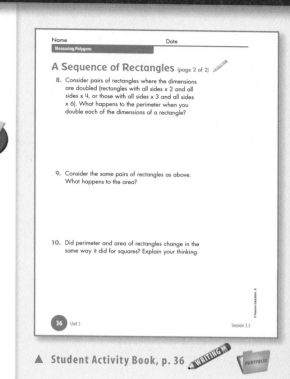

Name _____ Date _____
Measuring Polygons

A Sequence of Rectangles (page 2 of 2)

8. Consider pairs of rectangles where the dimensions are doubled (rectangles with all sides × 2 and all sides × 4, or those with all sides × 3 and all sides × 6). What happens to the perimeter when you double each of the dimensions of a rectangle?

9. Consider the same pairs of rectangles as above. What happens to the area?

10. Did perimeter and area of rectangles change in the same way it did for squares? Explain your thinking.

36 Unit 5   Session 2.3

▲ Student Activity Book, p. 36

Differentiation

2 English Language Learners In the previous session, students were asked to double the measurements of squares. In this activity, English Language Learners will need to know other multiplication-related words, such as *triple* and *quadruple*. To help students keep track of these terms, you can create a chart to hang in the classroom. On the chart, write *"double* = × 2", *"triple* = × 3", etc. You can meet with a small group of English Language Learners to introduce the chart. You already know that *double* means *times two.* What do you think *triple* means? (times three) What about *quadruple?* (times four) These are words you will need to know as we compare squares and rectangles.

Extension Students who easily see the patterns evolving in the rectangles can be challenged to predict the measurements for much larger rectangles, such as those 25, 50, or 100 times the original.

DISCUSSION

2 Comparing Rectangles and Squares

15 MIN   CLASS

Math Focus Points for Discussion

◆ Comparing the perimeters and areas of rectangles when the dimensions are multiplied by given amounts 2

Ask volunteers to provide their answers for the measurements of rectangles #2 and #4, and rectangles #3 and #6 on *Student Activity Book* page 35. Record these measurements on the board or overhead. All students should participate in the discussion even if some have not found the measurements for all six rectangles.

Dimensions	Perimeter	Area
6 inches by 8 inches	28 inches	48 square inches
12 inches by 16 inches	56 inches	192 square inches
9 inches by 12 inches	42 inches	108 square inches
18 inches by 24 inches	84 inches	432 square inches

In question #10, you were asked to think about whether these changes were the same as they were when we increased the dimensions of squares. When we worked with squares, you told me that if the dimensions of the sides were doubled, the perimeter doubled and the area quadrupled. Is the same thing true with rectangles? When you doubled each dimension, what happened to the perimeter? To the area?

Have students explain their thinking. Students should notice that the same thing is true: when the dimensions of a rectangle are doubled, the perimeter doubles and the area quadruples.

Students might say:

"At first I thought it was only true with squares because each side was the same length. But then when I started doing this I realized of course it was true of these rectangles, too. And since squares are rectangles too, it makes sense."

"It's just the same with rectangles as with squares. If you draw the rectangle, and then double each dimension, you can use four of the original rectangles to make the new one. So the area increases four times."

Here's one last question for you to think about. Why do you think this happens? If the perimeter doubles, why does the area quadruple? Talk about your ideas with a neighbor.

Give students time to discuss this with neighbors, and then solicit student ideas.

Students might say:

"When we were looking at the squares yesterday, we said that the perimeter only doubles because if you make the new square with four of the original squares, not every edge of each square is part of the perimeter of the bigger square. But since you use four squares to make it, the area is four times bigger. The same things happen with rectangles—with both the perimeter and the area."

"You know, it's because perimeter and area are different things. Perimeter is something around the shape. If you thought about a string, it makes sense perimeter only doubles. You could cut a string to show the length of each side of a rectangle, and then cut another string twice as long for each side of the rectangle. So you can sort of see why the perimeter is doubled. Perimeter is like a line, and if you double each part of it, the whole part is doubled."

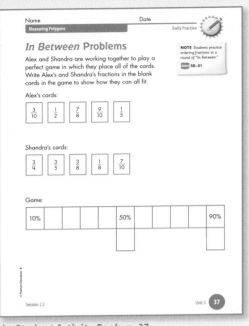

▲ **Student Activity Book, p. 37**

▲ **Student Activity Book, p. 38**

"You multiply to find area and you add when you find perimeter."

While students may not be able to articulate exactly why this change happens, there is one key idea that should emerge from this discussion:

Perimeter and area measure different attributes of a 2-D shape so they act differently. Perimeter is linear, or 1-dimensional, and area is 2-dimensional, and so these measurements change in different ways.

SESSION FOLLOW-UP
3 Daily Practice and Homework

Daily Practice: For ongoing review, have students complete *Student Activity Book* page 37.

Homework: Students draw a sequence of related rectangles and find their perimeter and area on *Student Activity Book* page 38.

Student Math Handbook: Students and families may use *Student Math Handbook* page 102 for reference and review. See pages 170–173 in the back of this unit.

Different Perimeter, Same Area

Math Focus Points

◆ Creating different rectangles with the same area but different perimeters

◆ Understanding square units as a unit of measure

Today's Plan		Materials
❶ ACTIVITY **Rearranging Rectangles**	30 MIN INDIVIDUALS	• *Student Activity Book,* p. 39 • M18 • Square tiles (as needed); scissors; tape (optional)
❷ DISCUSSION **Why Is the Area the Same?**	10 MIN CLASS	• *Student Activity Book,* p. 39
❸ ACTIVITY **One More Cut**	10 MIN PAIRS	• *Student Activity Book,* p. 39
❹ DISCUSSION **Square Units**	10 MIN CLASS	
❺ SESSION FOLLOW-UP **Daily Practice and Homework**		• *Student Activity Book,* pp. 40–41 • *Student Math Handbook,* p. 102

Ten-Minute Math

Quick Images: 2-D Show Images 17 and 18 of *Quick Images: 2-D* (T56) one at a time and follow the procedure for the basic routine. For each image, students discuss how they drew their figures, including any revisions they made after each viewing.

Ask students:

• How did you remember the parts of the image?

• What did you notice about the relationship of the parts of the image?

• What helped you remember the whole image so that you could draw your design?

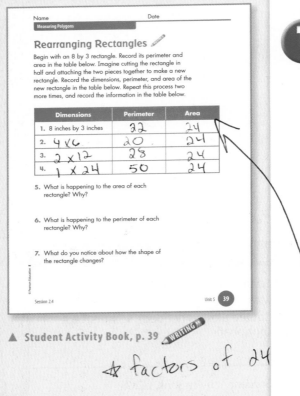

Name _____ Date _____
Measuring Polygons

Rearranging Rectangles

Begin with an 8 by 3 rectangle. Record its perimeter and area in the table below. Imagine cutting the rectangle in half and attaching the two pieces together to make a new rectangle. Record the dimensions, perimeter, and area of the new rectangle in the table below. Repeat this process two more times, and record the information in the table below.

	Dimensions	Perimeter	Area
1.	8 inches by 3 inches	22	24
2.	4 x 6	20	24
3.	2 x 12	28	24
4.	1 x 24	50	24

5. What is happening to the area of each rectangle? Why?

6. What is happening to the perimeter of each rectangle? Why?

7. What do you notice about how the shape of the rectangle changes?

Session 2.4   Unit 5 **39**

▲ Student Activity Book, p. 39 WRITING

☆ factors of 24

ACTIVITY

30 MIN   INDIVIDUALS

1 Rearranging Rectangles

In the first three sessions of this Investigation, students examined how area and perimeter change when the dimensions of a rectangle change. In this session, students continue to think about the differences between these two measurements—in this case how a rectangle can maintain the same area while the perimeter changes. In the next two sessions, students will consider rectangles that maintain the same perimeter while the area changes.

Begin the session by drawing an 8 by 3 rectangle on the board or overhead and labeling its dimensions. Ask students to find the perimeter and area of this rectangle and to record their answers on *Student Activity Book* page 39.

Draw a line across the middle of the rectangle and show how the rectangle can be rearranged to form a new rectangle.

Imagine that we're going to cut the rectangle in half and attach the two pieces together like this:

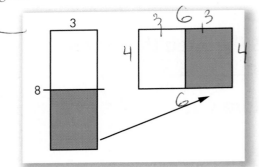

Ask students what the dimensions of the new rectangle are. If they seem uncertain, relabel the longer dimension on the original rectangle as shown below, and ask how that helps them determine the dimensions of the new rectangle.

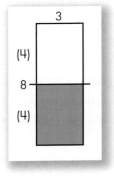

Have students work individually to complete *Student Activity Book* page 39, finding and recording the perimeter and area of the 4 by 6 rectangle, and "rearranging" this rectangle to form a 2 by 12 rectangle and then a 1 by 24 rectangle.

ONGOING ASSESSMENT: Observing Students at Work

Students create a sequence of rectangles, maintaining the same area while the perimeter changes.

- **Are students able to accurately determine perimeter and area?** What methods are they using? (e.g., For perimeter, are they adding all four of the sides, or adding two sides and doubling?) Do they record their answer using the correct unit of measure—either inches or square inches?

- **Do students recognize that the area remains constant?** How do they explain why the area remains the same?

- **Do students recognize that the perimeter is changing?** How do they explain why the perimeter changes?

DIFFERENTIATION: Supporting the Range of Learners

Intervention Some students will benefit from working with a partner on this activity. Students may also find it helpful to draw the rectangles on grid paper, cut them out, and tape them together, or to build the rectangles with square tiles.

Some students find it helpful to represent the problem using manipulatives.

Extension Students who finish quickly and understand how the perimeter changes with each rectangle can be challenged by asking them to do the activity again, only using a vertical cut. (The dimensions of the new rectangles would be 16 by $1\frac{1}{2}$, 32 by $\frac{3}{4}$, and 64 by $\frac{3}{8}$.)

DISCUSSION

2 Why Is the Area the Same?

10 MIN   CLASS

Math Focus Points for Discussion

◆ Creating different rectangles with the same area, but different perimeter

Ask students to share their answers for problems 5–7 on *Student Activity Book* page 39.

[Alicia] says that the area of all 4 of these rectangles is 24 square inches. Who can explain why that is?

Students might say:

"All the numbers are factors of 24. 3 × 8 equals 24, 4 × 6 equals 24, 2 × 12 equals 24."

"You never change how much space the rectangle covers—you just arrange it differently. But it's always the same amount."

[Alex] says that the perimeter is different every time. Who can explain that? . . . Was there anything you noticed about the shapes of the rectangles and their perimeter?

Students might say:

"When you cut the rectangle and change it, you're making more perimeter. Even though one side is getting shorter, the other side gets a lot longer."

"The skinnier a rectangle is, the more perimeter it has."

③ ACTIVITY
One More Cut

10 MIN   PAIRS

Here's one more question for you to work on with a partner. The last rectangle we imagined was 1 inch by 24 inches. Draw this rectangle on paper, and imagine making one more cut. What would the dimensions of the rectangle be? What would its perimeter and area be?

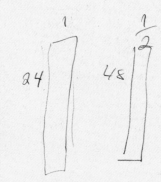

ONGOING ASSESSMENT: Observing Students at Work ✓

Students find the perimeter and area of a $\frac{1}{2}$ inch by 48 inch rectangle.

- **Are students able to accurately determine the dimensions of the new rectangle? ($\frac{1}{2}$ inch by 48 inches)**

- **Are students able to accurately determine the perimeter (97 inches) and area (24 square inches) of the new rectangle?** If not, what is confusing them?

DIFFERENTIATION: Supporting the Range of Learners ✴

Extension Students can be challenged to extend the sequence of rectangles ($\frac{1}{4}$ by 96, $\frac{1}{8}$ by 192, and so on).

④ DISCUSSION
Square Units

10 MIN   CLASS

Math Focus Points for Discussion

◆ Understanding square units as a unit of measure

Ask students to explain how they found the area of the rectangle.

Students might say:

"The area is still the same, 24 square inches. It's still the same amount of stuff."

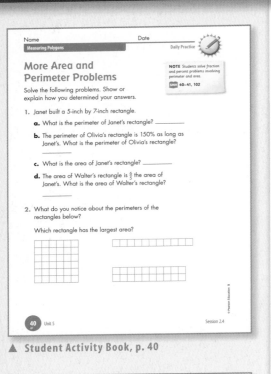

▲ Student Activity Book, p. 40

▲ Student Activity Book, p. 41

Ask the following question to help students consider that while area is measured in square units, it is not necessary to have complete squares:

Everyone agrees that the area is 24 square inches. But how can that be? 24 of our square tiles wouldn't fit in this skinny rectangle. Talk to a neighbor about how to explain this.

Give students time to discuss this and then solicit student responses.

Students might say:

"We didn't change the area at all, so it still has to be 24 square inches."

"You can see it's 24 square inches—we did it on grid paper so each little grid is now $\frac{1}{2}$ by 1, so if you put two of them together it makes one square. So it would make 24 all together."

Encourage students to ask questions of each other and to think about the explanations, and then summarize the idea for students.

When we find area, the standard unit of measure we use is a square unit. That doesn't mean the shape has to be a square or rectangle. We can find the area of any 2-D figure, regardless of its shape. Area is the amount of space something covers, and the standard unit of measure we use is a square unit, even when we are counting parts of square units.

SESSION FOLLOW-UP
⑤ Daily Practice and Homework

 Daily Practice: For ongoing review, have students complete *Student Activity Book* page 40.

Homework: On *Student Activity Book* page 41, students solve problems in which they are given certain perimeters and find other perimeters that are fractions or percentages of the originals.

Student Math Handbook: Students and families may use *Student Math Handbook* page 102 for reference and review. See pages 170–173 in the back of this unit.

Measuring Rectangles

Math Focus Points

◆ Creating different rectangles with the same area but different perimeters

◆ Creating different rectangles with the same perimeter but different areas

Today's Plan		Materials
① ACTIVITY **Introducing Fencing a Garden** 20 MIN · PAIRS · CLASS		• Square tiles (as needed) • M18 (as needed)
② MATH WORKSHOP **Measuring Rectangles** 40 MIN **2A** Fencing a Garden **2B** Rearranging a 16 by 12 Rectangle **2C** *LogoPaths* Activity: *Rhombuses and Parallelograms*		**2A** • *Student Activity Book*, p. 43 • M18 (as needed) • Square tiles **2B** • *Student Activity Book*, p. 44 • M18 • Square tiles **2C** • Computers with *LogoPaths* Software installed • M2–M3 (from Session 2.2)
③ SESSION FOLLOW-UP **Daily Practice**		• *Student Activity Book*, p. 45 • *Student Math Handbook*, p. 102

Ten-Minute Math

Quick Survey For the survey, ask the class "What was the main course you ate for dinner last night?" or a different categorical question that you or the students choose. Make sure they collect data about something they already know or can observe easily and is likely to change on a different day. Agree on a classification of 3–4 categories for the data and make a bar graph. Keep the class data to use for comparison in the next session. Ask students:

• What do you notice about the data?

• What do the data tell us about our class?

ACTIVITY

① Introducing Fencing a Garden

In the last session, students studied rectangles where the area remained constant while the perimeter changed. This activity introduces work on rectangles in which the perimeter remains constant and the area changes, which is studied further in the Math Workshop.

Imagine that you are going to plant a small garden. You have 12 feet of fencing to put around this garden. The only requirements are that the garden has to be a rectangle, and you have to use whole numbers for each dimension of the fence. Work with a partner to find out how many different rectangles you can make with 12 feet of fencing. Write down the dimensions and the area of each of these rectangles.

Students may use color tiles or graph paper to solve the problems. When most students have finished working, ask students to share the dimensions and area of the rectangles. Write these on the board.

Dimensions:	Area:
1 ft by 5 ft	5 square feet
2 ft by 4 ft	8 square feet
3 ft by 3 ft	9 square feet

Ask students how they found the rectangles. As students explain their strategies, help them clarify what they did.

Student strategies are likely to include the following:

- Trial and error—randomly drawing rectangles or moving around square tiles

- Realizing that the dimensions of the rectangle (the length and width) must sum to six

As students notice patterns, their solutions become more systematic.

Name _____ Date _____

Measuring Polygons

Fencing a Garden

Ms. Light's fifth-grade class will plant a garden in the school yard. The garden must be a rectangle, and the principal has given them 30 feet of fencing. Each side of the rectangle has to be a whole number.

Use grid paper, color tiles, or drawings to design at least 4 garden plots that would be enclosed by 30 feet of fence. Find the area for each garden plot.

Attach drawings of your rectangular gardens to this sheet. After you have designed at least four, fill out the table and answer the questions.

Dimensions	Perimeter	Area
1.	30 feet	
2.	30 feet	
3.	30 feet	
4.	30 feet	
5.	30 feet	
6.	30 feet	
7.	30 feet	

8. What are the dimensions of the rectangle with the largest area?

9. What are the dimensions of the rectangle with the smallest area?

10. What do you notice about the shape of these rectangles?

Sessions 2.5, 2.6　　Unit 5　43

▲ Student Activity Book, p. 43

In Math Workshop today, you're going to be making more rectangles. Some rectangles will have the same perimeter like the ones we just made. Other rectangles will have all the same area.

MATH WORKSHOP

🕐 40 MIN

2 Measuring Rectangles

Students find perimeters and areas of rectangles and examine how these measurements are related and how they are different. Students may also work on the *LogoPaths* activity, *Rhombuses and Parallelograms*. Students may choose to work either with a partner or individually on any of the activities in this Math Workshop.

2A Fencing a Garden

PAIRS   INDIVIDUALS

Have students work on *Student Activity Book* page 43. Students build rectangles (using whole numbers) that have a perimeter of 30 feet. They find the rectangles that have the smallest and the greatest areas.

Students are likely to begin work on this activity using trial and error. As they work, encourage them to become more systematic in their approach, asking questions such as:

What are the dimensions of the rectangles you've found so far? Is there any way you can use that information to find more rectangles?

Student Activity Book, p. 44 (reproduced)

Name _____ Date _____

Measuring Polygons

Rearranging a 16 by 12 Rectangle ✏️

Here is a 16-inch by 12-inch rectangle:

12

16

Record its perimeter and area in the table below.
Imagine cutting the rectangle in half, and attaching
the two pieces together to make a new rectangle.
Record the dimensions, perimeter, and area of the new
rectangle in the table below. Do the same process at
least three more times, and record the information in
the table below.

Dimensions	Perimeter	Area
1. 16 inches by 12 inches		
2. 8 × 46		
3. 4 × 3		
4. 2 × 1		
5.		

6. What is happening to the area of each rectangle? Why?

7. What is happening to the perimeter of each rectangle? Why?

8. What do you notice about how the shape of the
rectangle changes?

44   Unit 5   Sessions 2.5, 2.6

▲ **Student Activity Book, p. 44** WRITING

ONGOING ASSESSMENT: Observing Students at Work

Students find rectangles with a perimeter of 30 feet.

- **How do students find dimensions of rectangles?** Do they
randomly draw and make rectangles until they find ones that have a
perimeter of 30? Do they use the sum of the dimensions (length +
width = 15)? Do they notice and use patterns in the dimensions?

- **What do students notice about the area of the rectangles?** Do
they notice that the closer the dimensions are to each other, the
greater the area (e.g., A 1-inch by 14-inch rectangle has an area of 14
square inches. A 7-inch by 8-inch rectangle has an area of 56 square
inches.)? Do they notice that the closer the dimensions are to each
other, the closer the rectangle is to being a square?

DIFFERENTIATION: Supporting the Range of Learners

Intervention Ask students who are using trial and error throughout
this activity to list the dimensions of the rectangles they have made,
and to notice any patterns that might help them (e.g., the sum of the
length and width is 15). Also consider telling these students one of the
dimensions of a rectangle and having them figure out what the other
dimension would be to create a perimeter of 30.

Extension Students needing a challenge should start with 36 feet
of fencing. Challenge them to find all possible rectangles (using whole
numbers).

2B Rearranging a 16 by 12 Rectangle

PAIRS INDIVIDUALS

On *Student Activity Book* page 44, students begin with a 16 by 12
rectangle and find its perimeter and area. They make a succession of new
rectangles by imagining the rectangle cut in half horizontally, and the
two pieces put together.

ONGOING ASSESSMENT: Observing Students at Work

Students create a sequence of rectangles, maintaining the same area while the perimeter changes.

- **Are students able to accurately determine perimeter and area?** Do they record their answer using the correct unit of measure— either inches or square inches?

- **Do students recognize that the area remains constant?** How do they explain why the area remains the same?

- **Do students recognize that the perimeter is changing?** How do they explain why the perimeter changes?

DIFFERENTIATION: Supporting the Range of Learners

Intervention Some students may need to draw a rectangle on grid paper and actually cut it apart and rearrange it to see how the perimeter changes.

2C LogoPaths: Rhombuses and Parallelograms

PAIRS INDIVIDUALS

For complete details about this activity, see Session 2.2, pages 79–80.

Name _____ **Date** _____

Measuring Polygons   Daily Practice

Garden Dimensions

Solve the following problems. Show or explain how you determined your answers.

NOTE Students determine the dimensions of gardens when given the area and the perimeter.

102

Alicia, Charles, and Yumiko all planted gardens using 36 feet of fencing for the perimeter.

1. The area of Alicia's garden is 81 square feet. What are the dimensions of her garden?

2. The area of Charles's garden is 45 square feet. What are the dimensions of his garden?

3. The area of Yumiko's garden is 72 square feet. What are the dimensions of her garden?

Ongoing Review

4. Which of the following figures is **not** a regular polygon?

   A.   B.   C.   D.

Session 2.5   Unit 5   45

▲ **Student Activity Book, p. 45**

SESSION FOLLOW-UP
③ Daily Practice

Daily Practice: For reinforcement of this unit's content, have students complete *Student Activity Book* page 45.

Student Math Handbook: Students and families may use *Student Math Handbook* page 102 for reference and review. See pages 170–173 in the back of this unit.

Assessment: Perimeter and Area of Rectangles

Math Focus Points

◆ Creating different rectangles with the same area but different perimeters

◆ Creating different rectangles with the same perimeter but different areas

◆ Describing the shapes of rectangles that have the same area or the same perimeter

Today's Plan		Materials
① MATH WORKSHOP **Measuring Rectangles** **1A** Fencing a Garden **1B** Rearranging a 16 by 12 Rectangle **1C** *LogoPaths* Activity: *Rhombuses and Parallelograms*	30 MIN PAIRS	**1A** • *Student Activity Book,* p. 43 • M18 (as needed) • Square tiles **1B** • *Student Activity Book,* p. 44 • M18 • Square tiles **1C** • Computers with *LogoPaths* software installed • M2–M3 (from Session 2.2)
② DISCUSSION **Describing Rectangles**	15 MIN CLASS	• *Student Activity Book,* p. 43 (from Session 2.5)
③ ASSESSMENT ACTIVITY **Assessment: Perimeter and Area of Rectangles**	✓ 15 MIN INDIVIDUALS	• M19* • M18 (as needed) • Square tiles (as needed)
④ SESSION FOLLOW-UP **Daily Practice and Homework**		• *Student Activity Book,* pp. 46–47 • *Student Math Handbook,* p. 102

*See *Materials to Prepare,* p. 69.

Ten-Minute Math

Quick Survey For the survey, collect data about the same question you used in the previous session (What was the main course you ate for dinner last night?). Add today's data to the bar graph created in the last session and ask students to make comparisons.

Ask students: What do you notice about our data today? How are the data the same as last session's? How are they different? What do they tell us about our class?

MATH WORKSHOP

1 Measuring Rectangles

30 MIN

Students continue to find the perimeter and area of rectangles and examine how these measurements are related or not related. As students work today, they should be thinking about what is the same and what is different in rectangles that have a constant perimeter and in rectangles that have a constant area.

Today while you are working, think about what is the same and different about the rectangles you are making. Some of them have the same perimeter and some have the same area. One thing to think about is which rectangles have a lot of perimeter, and which ones have a lot of area.

1A Fencing a Garden

PAIRS INDIVIDUALS

For complete details about this activity, see Session 2.5, pages 96–97.

1B Rearranging a 16 by 12 Rectangle

PAIRS INDIVIDUALS

For complete details about this activity, see Session 2.5, pages 98–99.

1C LogoPaths: Rhombuses and Parallelograms

PAIRS INDIVIDUALS

For complete details about this activity, see Session 2.2, pages 79–80.

DISCUSSION

2 Describing Rectangles

15 MIN CLASS

Math Focus Points for Discussion

◆ Describing the shapes of rectangles that have the same area or the same perimeter

Begin the discussion by asking students about their answers on *Student Activity Book* page 43.

First you were asked to think about the connections between the areas of the rectangles and the perimeter. For all of these rectangles, the perimeter was 30. What were the dimensions of the rectangle that had the largest area? *(7 inches by 8 inches)* What were the dimensions of the rectangle with the smallest area? *(1 inch by 14 inches)* If we use only whole numbers, are these the largest and smallest rectangles with a perimeter of 30 inches? How do you know?

Students should realize that if only whole numbers can be used, these are the largest and smallest rectangles.

What did you notice about the shapes of these rectangles and the area?

Students should notice that the greater the area, the closer the rectangle is to being a square. They are likely to describe the rectangles with less area as being "long and skinny."

A student explains how the areas of rectangles change if the perimeters are the same.

[Cecilia] is saying that she thinks that when the perimeter stays the same, the rectangle with the largest area will be closest to a square. Do people agree or disagree? Why?

Continue the discussion by asking students about their answers on *Student Activity Book* page 44.

What did you notice about the area of all these rectangles? *(Area remains the same.)* What about the perimeter? . . . Which rectangle had the greatest perimeter? *(1 by 192)*

Students should notice that as the rectangle gets "rearranged," the perimeter is increasing significantly even as the area remains the same. (The perimeter changes from 56 inches to 386 inches.) Students should notice that there is much more perimeter to measure as the dimensions get farther apart.

Let's think about these rectangles. When we kept the perimeter the same, [Cecilia] said the rectangle that was closest to a square had the largest area. Since all of these rectangles have the same area, we can't say that. But what could we say?

Students should notice a similar situation; that the rectangle that has the smallest perimeter (56 inches—the 12 by 16 rectangle) is the rectangle closest to a square, and that the rectangle with the greatest perimeter (386 inches—the 1 by 192 rectangle) is "long and skinny."

[Tavon] says that it's sort of the same thing. He says that if the area is the same, the long and skinny rectangles have the greatest perimeter. He's making a conjecture that the closer a rectangle is to a square, the area is greater, but the perimeter is less. What do people think about this?

Solicit student responses. At this point, the two important ideas for students to understand are how to find perimeters and areas of rectangles, and that perimeter and area measure different attributes of a rectangle.

Professional Development

❶ **Teacher Note:** Assessment: Perimeter and Area of Rectangles, p. 149

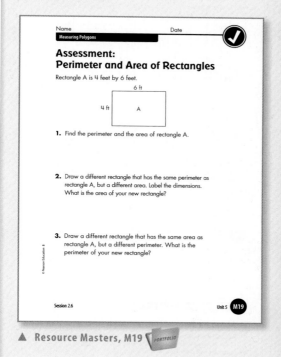

▲ **Resource Masters, M19**

ASSESSMENT ACTIVITY

③ Perimeter and Area of Rectangles

15 MIN   INDIVIDUALS

Have students complete Assessment: Perimeter and Area of Rectangles (M19) individually.❶ They are given a 4 by 6 rectangle and asked to find its perimeter and area. They draw two new rectangles—one that has a perimeter of 20 feet, but a different area, and one that has an area of 24 square feet, but a different perimeter.

This assessment addresses Benchmark 3: Determine the perimeter and area of rectangles.

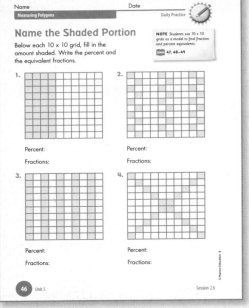

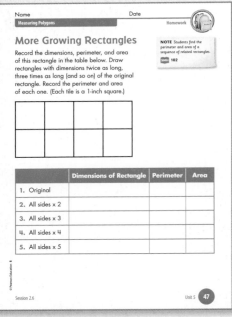

▲ Student Activity Book, p. 46

▲ Student Activity Book, p. 47

ONGOING ASSESSMENT: Observing Students at Work

Students find the perimeter and area of related rectangles.

- **How do students find the perimeter and area?**

- **How do students create a different rectangle with the same perimeter?** Do they use trial and error until they find a rectangle with a perimeter of 20 inches? Or are they more efficient and realize that they can use any rectangle whose dimensions sum to 10? (e.g., 1 by 9, 2 by 8, 3 by 7, or 5 by 5)

- **How do students create a different rectangle with the same area?** Do they use trial and error (drawing or using square tiles) until they find a rectangle with an area of 24 square inches? Or are they more efficient and realize that they can use any rectangle whose dimensions are factors of 24? (e.g., 1 by 24, 2 by 12, or 3 by 8)

DIFFERENTIATION: Supporting the Range of Learners

Intervention Encourage students who are still developing their ideas to use square tiles or grid paper to help them complete this assessment.

SESSION FOLLOW-UP

 ## Daily Practice and Homework

 Daily Practice: For ongoing review, have students complete *Student Activity Book* page 46.

Homework: On *Student Activity Book* page 47, students draw a sequence of related rectangles and find their perimeter and area.

Student Math Handbook: Students and families may use *Student Math Handbook* page 102 for reference and review. See pages 170–173 in the back of this unit.

Mathematical Emphasis

Features of Shape Creating and describing similar shapes

Math Focus Points

◆ Recognizing and building similar figures

◆ Examining the relationship among angles, line lengths, and areas of similar polygons

◆ Making a generalization about the change in areas of similar figures

◆ Building similar figures for polygons made from two or more Power Polygon pieces

◆ Using Power Polygons to find the areas of similar hexagons

Similarity

	Student Activity Book	Student Math Handbook	Professional Development: Read Ahead of Time	
SESSION 3.1 p. 108				
Building Similar Polygons Students build figures that are mathematically similar to some of the Power Polygon pieces. They examine how many of the same polygon pieces it takes to build the larger, similar figures.	49–51	103–104	• **Teacher Note:** Similar Shapes, p. 152	
SESSION 3.2 p. 114				
Building More Similar Shapes Students begin a Math Workshop where they continue investigating similarity, including building similar hexagons. In a *LogoPaths* activity, they use their understanding of similarity to determine whether pairs of polygons are similar or not similar.	49, 53–56	103–104	• **Dialogue Box:** Building Similar Hexagons, p. 167	
SESSION 3.3 p. 124				
Building More Similar Shapes, *continued* Students discuss the relationship between side length and area of similar figures. They continue to focus on similarity as they work on the Math Workshop. They begin creating "Similarity Posters."	49, 53–54, 57–59	102, 103–104	• **Teacher Note:** Building Larger Similar Figures, p. 153	
SESSION 3.4 p. 129				
Similarity Posters Students discuss how the areas of similar hexagons change. They complete their similarity posters.	53–54, 57, 61–62	103–104		
SESSION 3.5 p. 133				
End-of-Unit Assessment Students are assessed on their understanding of material in the unit. They also present their similarity posters in small groups.	63	103–104	• **Teacher Note:** End-of-Unit Assessment, p. 155	

Ten-Minute Math See page 16 for an overview.

Quick Images: 2-D
- T57, *Quick Images: 2-D* 🖥 Set aside images 19–22 for this Investigation.

Quick Survey
- **No materials needed**

Materials to Gather	Materials to Prepare
• **Power Polygons** (2 sets, distributed evenly among groups of 3 or 4 students)	
• **Power Polygons** (2 sets, distributed evenly among groups of 3 or 4 students)	• **M4, *LogoPaths: Polygon Pairs*** Make copies. (3 per student) • **Chart paper** Label the chart paper, "Ways to Make Hexagon H" • **Computers with *LogoPaths* software installed**
• **M4, *LogoPaths: Polygon Pairs*** (from Session 3.2; optional) • **Power Polygons** (2 sets, distributed evenly among groups of 3 or 4 students) • **Chart paper** • **Markers, colored pencils, crayons**	• **Chart paper** Prepare a two column table with the titles, "When the sides are this many times as long…" and "The area is this many times as large…" • **Computers with *LogoPaths* software installed**
• **M4, *LogoPaths: Polygon Pairs*** (from Session 3.2; optional) • **Power Polygons** (2 sets, distributed evenly among groups of 3 or 4 students) • **Chart paper** • **Markers, colored pencils, crayons**	• **Computers with *LogoPaths* software installed**
• **Similarity posters** (from Sessions 3.3 and 3.4)	• **M20–M22, End-of-Unit Assessment** Make copies. (1 per student)

🖥 Overhead Transparency

Building Similar Polygons

Math Focus Points

◆ Recognizing and building similar figures

◆ Examining the relationship among angles, line lengths, and areas of similar polygons

Vocabulary

similar

Today's Plan			Materials
① ACTIVITY **Introducing Similarity**	⏱ 15 MIN	👥 CLASS	• Power Polygons (2 sets, distributed evenly among groups of 3 or 4 students)
② ACTIVITY **Building Similar Polygons**	⏱ 30 MIN	👤 INDIVIDUALS	• *Student Activity Book*, p. 49 • Power Polygons (2 sets, distributed evenly among groups of 3 or 4 students)
③ DISCUSSION **Comparing Similar Figures**	⏱ 15 MIN	👥 CLASS	• *Student Activity Book*, p. 49
④ SESSION FOLLOW-UP **Daily Practice and Homework**			• *Student Activity Book*, pp. 50–51 • *Student Math Handbook*, pp. 103–104

Ten-Minute Math

Quick Images: 2-D Show Images 19 and 20 of *Quick Images: 2-D* (T57) one at a time and follow the procedure for the basic routine. For each image, students discuss how they drew their figures, including and revisions they made after each viewing. Ask students:

- How did you remember the parts of the image?
- What did you notice about the relationship of the parts of the image?
- What helped you remember the whole image so that you could draw your design?

ACTIVITY

1 Introducing Similarity

15 MIN   **CLASS**

Distribute sets of Power Polygons to each group of three or four students. Ask students to find triangles D, E, and F. Display these triangles on the overhead.❶ ❷

Take a look at these three triangles. Talk in your small groups about what is the same about these triangles, and what is different.

Give students a few minutes to discuss this, and then solicit student comments.❸

For what is the same, students may offer that all three triangles:

- Have the same angles (45–45–90)

- Are right triangles

- Have two sides the same length

- Have the same shape

For what is different, students might say

- They are different sizes

- One is smaller, one is in the middle, one is larger

- They are different colors

There is a special mathematical term to describe the relationship when polygons have the same shape but are not necessarily the same size: we say that these polygons are similar. We use the word *similar* in everyday speech to mean, "alike in some way." But when we use *similar* in math class, we mean alike in "this exact way"—the two polygons have the exact same shape but may have different sizes.❹

---

❶ **Teacher Note:** Similar Shapes, p. 152

Math Notes

❷ **Similar Shapes** Two figures are similar if they have exactly the same shape, even if one is larger than the other. In a pair of similar figures, the angles in one are the same as the angles in the other. However, the sides of the two figures are not the same; they are proportional. This proportion can be any multiplicative increase or decrease (2 times longer, 0.5 as long). Because students are using the Power Polygons, the proportions of the pairs of similar figures built are whole numbers (2 times as large, 3 times, etc.)

❸ **Defining *Shape*** The word *shape* is used in different ways. For example, when we say, "This shape is a rectangle" we are using the term *shape* as a synonym for *figure* or *geometric object*. In discussing similarity, the term *shape* is used in a very specific way to identify the outline or form of a figure. Using this definition, a long and skinny rectangle does not have the same shape as a more squarelike rectangle, but a 3 by 4 rectangle has the same shape as a 6 by 8 rectangle. In this Investigation, when students are asked whether figures have the same shape, it means the shapes are in proportion to each other, like photos that are reduced or enlarged.

❹ **Congruence and Similarity** When two geometric figures have the same shape (meaning they are similar) and the same size, those figures are congruent (having the same size and shape). The relationship between congruence and similarity is nested—all pairs of congruent figures are also similar, but not all pairs of similar figures are congruent.

Teaching Note

⑤ Visually Checking for Similarity One way to check for similarity is by standing directly over a shape that is built, closing one eye, and holding the original shape above it. Then, move the original shape up or down to see whether you can align all of its sides with the original shape. Demonstrate this for students, but caution them that this method is not completely precise—if the angles or sides are only slightly different, it may not show similarity.

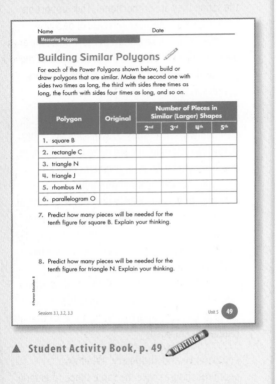

▲ Student Activity Book, p. 49

We often use the word *similar* when we want to say that something is like something else. [Janet] and [Olivia] have *similar* hair, because it is brown. [Janet's] hair is straight, and [Olivia's] hair is curly, so their hair is not *exactly* alike, but there are *similarities*.

Explain that the concept of *similar* is a little different when referring to polygons.

When we talk about *similar* squares or rectangles, we look for characteristics that *are* exactly alike, such as the measurement of angles. The polygons may be different sizes, but if they have the exact same shape, we still refer to them as *similar*.

On the overhead, build two rectangles made from Power Polygon C, and ask students to build the same rectangles.

Ask students whether these two rectangles are similar and to explain why or why not. Expect some students to say they are similar, because they are both rectangles. Help students to see that for a shape to be similar, the angles have to be the same, and that the lengths of the sides have to be multiplied (or divided) by the same number. Ask questions such as:

Are the angles the same? Do the lengths of the sides increase in the same way? [Georgia] says they're not similar because the top of the rectangle doubles, but the side stays the same length. What do people think? What would a similar rectangle look like?

Give students a minute or two to build a similar rectangle. If time remains, ask students to look at their set of Power Polygons to find similar polygons. (A and B are similar, as are I and N.)⑤

DIFFERENTIATION: Supporting the Range of Learners

ELL You can meet with English Language Learners separately to reinforce their language skills in talking about the mathematical concept of *similarity,* which they will use throughout this Investigation.

Some students find it helpful to check whether two polygons are similar by trying to align them visually.

⑥ Power Polygon Sets There are enough Power Polygon pieces for students to build the first few similar figures for each shape, and every student should build these shapes. It is likely there are not enough pieces for all students to build all shapes. For the larger similar shapes (those four times as large and up), encourage students to begin drawing the similar figures on blank paper. Some students will continue to benefit from using the Power Polygon pieces to build each shape.

⑦ Building Similar Polygons In some cases, the similar shapes can be made by using additional pieces and placing them next to the original shape. Rectangle C is an example of this. Similar rectangles can be constructed simply by replicating the Power Polygon piece C in the same orientation.

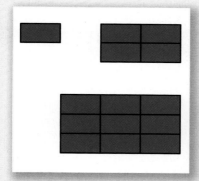

However, this is not always the case. With a triangle such as I, one of the triangular pieces must be oriented differently in order to replicate the shape of the original figure.

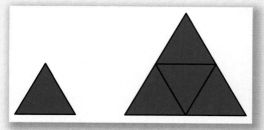

ACTIVITY
Building Similar Polygons

30 MIN INDIVIDUALS

Students begin *Student Activity Book* page 49.⑥

In the last Investigation, when you built a sequence of squares and rectangles, you were making similar figures. Today, you're going to use Power Polygon pieces to do the same thing.⑦

Let students know that at the end of the session today, they will be discussing problems 1–3. They will also be finding similar figures for squares, rectangles, and triangles. They continue working on Building Similar Polygons in the next session.

Students build, test, and record similar figures.

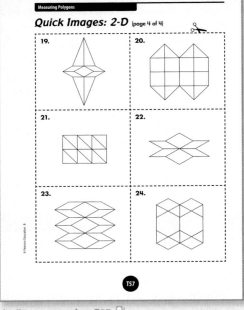

Measuring Polygons

Quick Images: 2-D (page 4 of 4)

19. 20.

21. 22.

23. 24.

T57

▲ Transparencies, T57

ONGOING ASSESSMENT: Observing Students at Work

Students build similar figures for given polygons.

- **Are students able to notice both the whole shape of the figures they build, as well as the way the whole shape is composed of smaller shapes?**

- **Are students able to show that the angles are the same in the larger figures and that the sides are two or three or four times as long?**

- **Do students notice that the number of smaller polygons that compose the larger figure is the same no matter what polygon they enlarge?** (e.g., If the sides are two times as long, four of the smaller polygons are needed, if the sides are three times as long, nine of the smaller polygons are needed, and so on.)

As students are working, call their attention to two components of similarity: the angles must be the same size, and each side has to be multiplied by the same amount. To help students think about the relationships between similar shapes, ask questions such as these.

- Are the angles in the similar shapes the same size? How do you know? How do you know the shapes are similar? How do you know each side of the larger shape is [two] times larger than the original?

- How many pieces does it take to make the larger shape? Do you see any patterns? Can you predict how many pieces you need for the next shape?

DIFFERENTIATION: Supporting the Range of Learners

Extension Students needing a challenge should consider how the perimeter and area change in each similar shape.

15 MIN   CLASS

DISCUSSION

3 Comparing Similar Figures

Math Focus Points for Discussion

◆ Examining the relationship among angles, line lengths, and areas of similar polygons

Ask one or two students to show how they built triangles similar to N with side lengths two, three, and four times as long. As each student builds the larger, similar triangle, ask them to explain how they know the shapes are similar, and how they know each side length is two or three or four times longer than the original triangle. Also ask the class to consider the area of the larger shapes.

If each side is two (or three or four or five) times longer, how many pieces does it take to build the larger shape?

Then ask students to consider the similar figures for square B, rectangle C, and triangle N.

What is the same about making larger shapes with square B, rectangle C, and triangle N? What is different?

Students might say:

"For each one, the second figure takes four of the figure to build, the third figure takes nine, the fourth figure takes sixteen, and the fifth figure takes twenty-five."

"When each side is doubled, the area is quadrupled."

"For the squares and rectangles, you just kept repeating the shapes, but for the triangle, sometimes you had to turn the triangle upside-down to make the larger shape."

If necessary, remind students that 4, 9, 16, 25, and so on are square numbers.

SESSION FOLLOW-UP
4 Daily Practice and Homework

 Daily Practice: For ongoing review, have students complete *Student Activity Book* page 50.

 Homework: Students use a clock face to add fractions on *Student Activity Book* page 51.

 Student Math Handbook: Students and families may use *Student Math Handbook* pages 103–104 for reference and review. See pages 170–173 in the back of this unit.

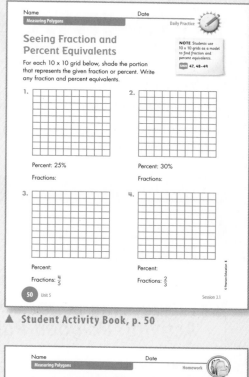
▲ Student Activity Book, p. 50

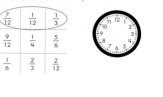
▲ Student Activity Book, p. 51

Building More Similar Shapes

Math Focus Points

◆ Recognizing and building similar figures

◆ Examining the relationship among angles, line lengths, and areas
  of similar polygons

Today's Plan		Materials
① **ACTIVITY** **Introducing Building Similar Hexagons**	🕐 15 MIN 👥 PAIRS 👨‍👩‍👧 CLASS	• Power Polygons (2 sets, distributed evenly among groups of 3 or 4 students) • Chart: "Ways To Make Hexagon H"*
② **ACTIVITY** **Introducing *LogoPaths* Activity: *Polygon Pairs***	👨‍👩‍👧 CLASS	• Computers with *LogoPaths* software installed
③ **MATH WORKSHOP** **Similar Polygons** **③A** Building Similar Polygons **③B** Building Similar Hexagons **③C** *LogoPaths* Activity: *Polygon Pairs*	🕐 45 MIN	**③A** • *Student Activity Book*, p. 49 (from Session 3.1) • Power Polygons (2 sets, distributed evenly among groups of 3 or 4 students) **③B** • *Student Activity Book*, pp. 53–54 • Power Polygons (2 sets, distributed evenly among groups of 3 or 4 students) **③C** • M4 (3 per student)* • Computers with *LogoPaths* software installed
④ **SESSION FOLLOW-UP** **Daily Practice and Homework**		• *Student Activity Book*, pp. 55–56 • *Student Math Handbook*, pp. 103–104

*See *Materials to Prepare,* p. 107.

Ten-Minute Math

Quick Images: 2-D Show Images 21 and 22 of *Quick Images: 2-D* (T57) one at a time and follow the procedure for the basic routine. For each image, students discuss how they drew their figures, incuding any revisions they made after each viewing. Ask students:

- How did you remember the parts of the image?
- What did you notice about the relationship of the parts of the image?
- What helped you remember the whole image so you could draw your design?

1 ACTIVITY

Introducing Building Similar Hexagons

15 MIN   CLASS   PAIRS

Professional Development

● **Dialogue Box:** Building Similar Hexagons, p. 167

In the Math Workshop in this session, students are asked to build similar hexagons. Because they must use other Power Polygon pieces (besides hexagon H) to do this, this introduction is intended to help students begin thinking about how hexagons can be decomposed into smaller shapes, while maintaining the same area.

Review the activity in the previous lesson, and introduce the idea of building similar hexagons. Place hexagon H on the overhead for this discussion.

In our last session, you looked at similar shapes for squares, rectangles, and triangles. You told me the same thing is happening—the second figure is four times larger than the original figure, the third figure is nine times larger, and so on. Do you think this is going to be true for a hexagon as well? Let's look at hexagon H. Can you picture in your mind how this shape would grow into a larger similar shape? Would a hexagon grow in the same way as a rectangle? What would be the same? What would be different?

Solicit student ideas. Expect some students to realize that the hexagon pieces cannot be used to build a larger, similar hexagon. Ask students to think about different Power Polygon pieces that can be used to make the same shape as hexagon H.

What Power Polygon pieces will fit together to make a shape exactly the same size and shape as hexagon H? How many different ways can you find? Work with your partner and record the different pieces you can use.

Give students time to find different combinations. Encourage them to draw each of the different possibilities, recording the different pieces they use.

Once work begins to subside, call the students back together. Ask for volunteers to share possible combinations. As students suggest combinations, ask whether everyone agrees that these pieces would form a hexagon that is the same size as hexagon H. If students disagree, have

Name _____ Date _____

Measuring Polygons

LogoPaths: Polygon Pairs

Are the polygons in each pair similar or not similar?
Explain how you know. Be sure to include the tools you
used (Label Turns, Label Lengths, Overlay commands)
to help you decide.

1. Polygon Pair #_____   Similar _____   Not Similar _____

2. Polygon Pair #_____   Similar _____   Not Similar _____

3. Polygon Pair #_____   Similar _____   Not Similar _____

M4 Unit 5

▲ **Resource Masters, M4**

students go to the overhead and build the hexagon to see whether the suggested combination works. If students agree, write the combination on the chart paper you prepared. Your chart might look something like the following:

> ## Ways to Make Hexagon H
>
> 6 of triangle N
>
> 3 of rhombus M
>
> 2 of trapezoid K
>
> 4 of triangle N and 1 of rhombus M
>
> 2 of triangle N and 2 of rhombus M
>
> 1 of trapezoid K, 1 of rhombus M and
>   1 of triangle N
>
> 1 of trapezoid K and 3 of triangle N

Let's say we're going to use one hexagon as the unit of area. What would be the area of each of these combinations?

Point to different combinations on the chart (such as two trapezoids, six triangles, and one trapezoid, two triangles, and one rhombus). Students should realize the area of each shape is one hexagon.

As you start the Math Workshop today, one of the new activities is to build similar hexagons. You may need to use shapes other than hexagons to build the next larger hexagons.

ACTIVITY

CLASS

2 Introducing *LogoPaths* Activity: *Polygon Pairs*

In this activity, students are shown pairs of polygons and asked to determine whether the polygons in each pair are similar to one another. They can use the **Label Turns** and **Label Lengths** tools and **Overlay** commands to help make this determination. Students then explain the reasoning behind their responses on *LogoPaths: Polygon Pairs* (M4).

To introduce this activity, open *Polygon Pairs* in the *LogoPaths* software, select Group 1 Level 1, and click on OK.

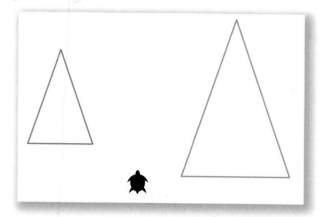

The *LogoPaths* activity you're learning today is called *Polygon Pairs*. Your job with this activity is to determine whether the polygons in each pair are similar or not similar. Look at this first pair of polygons. Talk to a partner for a minute about how you can tell whether the polygons in the pair are similar or not similar.

Ask a couple of volunteers to share their answers to this question.

Students might say:

"We think that the triangles are similar because the angles look exactly the same."

"We agree. Both triangles are the same shape, except the second triangle is bigger than the first."

To check for similarity, students can use the **Label Turns** tool. Demonstrate this by clicking on this feature.

So you think that these two triangles are similar because they have the same size angles. You can use the Label Turns tool to help you be sure that the angles are the same. What do you notice about the turns in these two triangles? What do the turns tell you about the size of the angles?

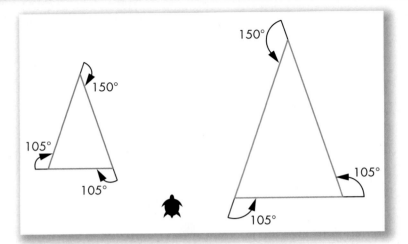

Students should notice that the turns are the same for both triangles, 150° at the top vertices and 105° at the bottom right and left vertices. Students should also recognize that since the turns are the same, the angles are also the same—one 30° angle and two 75° angles in each triangle.

Students can also use the **Label Lengths** tool to check for similarity. Demonstrate by clicking on this feature.

The Label Lengths tool can help you compare the sides of the polygons in each pair. What do you notice about the sides of the triangles in this pair?

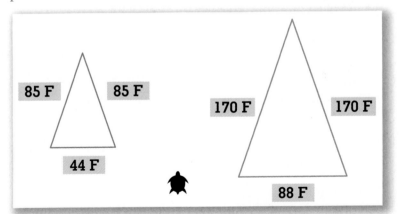

Students should notice that the sides of the red triangle are twice the lengths of the sides of the blue triangle.

You can use Overlay Commands to help you compare the angles and the sides of the polygons in each pair. If you look in the Teach panel, you'll see that there are three overlay commands for this polygon pair.

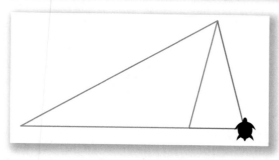

You can use the other overlay commands when you work on this pair in Math Workshop. Then you'll explain on your student sheet how you decided whether the polygons are similar or not similar.

Similar Polygons

45 MIN

In Math Workshop, students work on three activities: Building Similar Polygons, Building Similar Hexagons, and *LogoPaths: Polygon Pairs*. All three activities provide experiences building and comparing similar polygons. Students may work alone or with a partner on any of the activities in the Math Workshop.

3A Building Similar Polygons

PAIRS   INDIVIDUALS

Have students continue working on *Student Activity Book* page 49. Tell them to make sure they work on Questions 7 and 8 since these are discussed at the beginning of Session 3.3.

Some students will quickly see the pattern that emerges on the table and be tempted to just write in the numbers. Encourage all students to build or draw each of the shapes so they can see the progression of the shapes and how the length of the sides and the area increase.

ONGOING ASSESSMENT: Observing Students at Work

Students build similar shapes for given polygons.

- **Are students able to build each similar figure?**

- **Do students notice the patterns that emerge?** That each similar figure grows the same way, regardless of the shape?

- **Are students able to predict the 10th figure for the square and triangle?** Are they just thinking numerically (it would take 100 pieces) or are they able to describe the length of the sides of the 10th figure and visualize what the shape would look like?

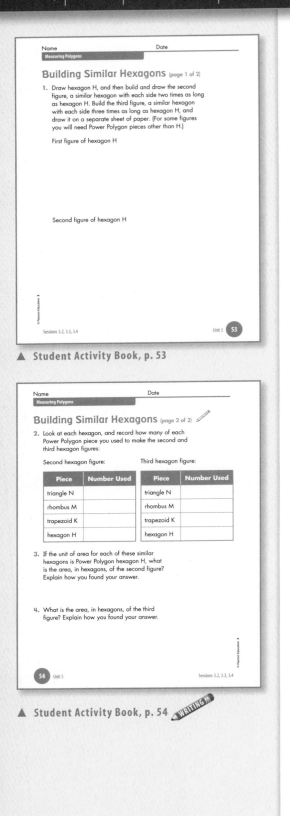

▲ **Student Activity Book, p. 53**

▲ **Student Activity Book, p. 54**

As you circulate, help students think about extending the patterns they have seen so far by asking questions such as:

- If you built the 10th square (or triangle), what would it look like? How long would each side be? How many pieces would it take to build it? How do you know?

DIFFERENTIATION: Supporting the Range of Learners

Intervention Some students will need to build the 10th square to be able to visualize what the larger square looks like.

Extension Students needing a challenge should consider how the perimeter is changing as well.

3B Building Similar Hexagons

PAIRS   INDIVIDUALS

Students draw Power Polygon H, a hexagon, and then build larger similar hexagons. Students record their work on *Student Activity Book* pages 53–54.

For this work, Power Polygon pieces other than the original shape must be used. For instance, it is not possible to build the second shape for hexagon H using only hexagons as suggested below:

As you circulate, you may want to remind students to look at the lists from the beginning of this session to find shapes that fit together to make a hexagon.

Students find a variety of ways to construct larger similar hexagons.

Once students have made the figures, they determine the area of the similar shapes using the area of one hexagon as the unit of measure.

ONGOING ASSESSMENT: Observing Students at Work

Students build larger similar hexagons.

- **Do students build similar hexagons?** How do they know the shapes are similar? Do they compare angles and sides? Or do they use a visual method? (If they use a visual method, they should also consider another way to show similarity.)

- **How do students build the similar hexagons?** Do they use trial and error with a combination of Power Polygon pieces? Or do they find a pattern of pieces they can use (e.g., using only trapezoids to build the second figure, using trapezoids and rhombuses for the third figure)?

- **Do students accurately record the number of each kind of piece they use to build similar hexagons?**

- **How do students find the area of the similar shapes using the hexagon as the unit of measure?** Do they use relationships among the Power Polygon pieces (e.g., two trapezoids or three rhombuses or six triangles have the same area as one hexagon)? Do they cover the figures with all of one kind of Power Polygon (e.g., the triangle)?

As you circulate, help students think about how to build similar hexagons by asking questions such as:

- Can you only use hexagons for this? How do you know?

- What other pieces might you use? Does the list we made earlier help you? How?

- How do you know the shapes are similar? Are the angles the same? How do you know? Are the sides of the new figure two (or three or four) times longer than the original hexagon? How do you know?

DIFFERENTIATION: Supporting the Range of Learners

Intervention Some students have difficulty finding the area of the similar shapes using the hexagon as a unit of measure. Have them decompose the figure and use the pieces to cover hexagons. Ask these students:

- How many hexagons do you think these pieces would cover?

Have them take this number of hexagons and try to exactly cover them using the pieces from the original similar shape.

Students cover copies of hexagon H with the smaller Power Polygon pieces in order to find the area of the larger figures.

3C *LogoPaths: Polygon Pairs*

PAIRS   INDIVIDUALS

Students work individually or in pairs for this *LogoPaths* activity. They are shown pairs of polygons and asked to determine whether the polygons in each pair are similar to one another. Have them explain the reasoning behind their responses on *LogoPaths: Polygon Pairs* (M4).

In the Math Workshops in this Investigation, students should work on *Polygon Pairs 1–8*.

ONGOING ASSESSMENT: Observing Students at Work

Students use their understanding of similar figures as having the same shape and not necessarily the same size to determine whether pairs of polygons are similar.

- **Are students able to identify which pairs of polygons are similar?** Are they able to do so even when the polygons in the pair have different orientations (e.g., in Pair 2 where two squares are shown, one large and one small, with the large square turned 45°, or in Pair 5 where two right triangles are shown with one sitting on its base and one on its hypotenuse)?

- **Are they able to identify which pairs are not similar (e.g., Pair 4, where a regular hexagon is shown along with a nonregular hexagon containing a pair of longer sides)?**

- **Are students able to use the turns to determine the angles of the polygons in each pair?** For example, if the turn is 105°, do they know that the interior angle is 75°?

- **Are students' explanations for identifying a pair as similar or not similar correct?**

SESSION FOLLOW-UP
Daily Practice and Homework

 Daily Practice: For reinforcement of this unit's content, have students complete *Student Activity Book* page 55.

Homework: On *Student Activity Book* page 56, students draw similar shapes with sides that are two or three times as long as the sides of the original shapes.

 Student Math Handbook: Students and families may use *Student Math Handbook* pages 103–104 for reference and review. See pages 170–173 in the back of this unit.

Name _____ Date _____
Measuring Polygons   Daily Practice

Similar Shapes on Grids

NOTE Students draw two similar shapes on grids with sides two times and three times as long as the sides of the original shapes.
SMH 103–104

1. Use the grid to draw a similar shape with sides that are two times as long. Find the area of both shapes.

   Area of original: _____
   Area of new shape: _____

2. Use the grid to draw a similar shape with sides that are three times as long. Count the triangles to find the area of both shapes.

   Area of original: _____
   Area of new shape: _____

Ongoing Review

3. Which polygon pair is **not** similar?

   A.   B.   C.

Session 3.2   Unit 5   55

▲ Student Activity Book, p. 55

Name _____ Date _____
Measuring Polygons   Homework

Drawing Similar Shapes
Use the grids for your drawings.
Find the area of each shape.

NOTE Students first draw similar shapes with sides that are 2 or 3 times as long as the sides of the original shape, and then find the perimeter and area of each shape.
SMH 102, 103–104

1. Draw a similar shape with each side that is 2 times as long.

   Area of original: _____   Area of new shape: _____

2. Draw a similar shape with each side that is 3 times as long.

   Area of original: _____   Area of new shape: _____

56   Unit 5   Session 3.2

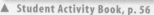
▲ Student Activity Book, p. 56

Building More Similar Shapes, *continued*

Math Focus Points

◆ Making a generalization about the change in areas of similar figures

◆ Building similar figures for polygons made from two or more Power Polygon pieces

◆ Using Power Polygons to find the areas of similar hexagons

Today's Plan		Materials
DISCUSSION **① About Growing Shapes**	15 MIN CLASS	• *Student Activity Book,* p. 49 (from Session 3.1) • Chart paper*
MATH WORKSHOP **② Similar Polygons** **②A** Building Similar Hexagons **②B** *LogoPaths* Activity: *Polygon Pairs* (optional) **②C** Making a Similarity Poster	45 MIN	**②A** • *Student Activity Book,* pp. 53–54 (from Session 3.2) • Power Polygons (2 sets, distributed evenly among groups of 3 or 4 students) **②B** • M4 (from Session 3.2) • Computers with *LogoPaths* software installed **②C** • *Student Activity Book,* p. 57 • Power Polygons (2 sets, distributed evenly among groups of 3 or 4 students); chart paper; markers; colored pencils; crayons
SESSION FOLLOW-UP **③ Daily Practice and Homework**		• *Student Activity Book,* pp. 58–59 • *Student Math Handbook,* pp. 102, 103–104

*See *Materials to Prepare,* p. 107.

Ten-Minute Math

Quick Survey For the survey, ask the class "How many states have you visited?" or a different numerical question that you or the students choose. Make sure they collect data about something they already know or can observe easily. With today's data, make a line plot. Ask students:

• What do you notice about the data?

• What do the data tell us about our class?

DISCUSSION

About Growing Shapes

15 MIN   CLASS

Math Focus Points for Discussion

◆ Making a generalization about the change in area of similar figures❶

This discussion focuses on Questions 7 and 8 of *Student Activity Book* page 49, which ask students to make predictions for the 10th triangle and square. First, review the work students have been doing.

When we first started working on this sheet, you noticed a pattern—that for the square, triangle, and rectangle, the second figure took four pieces to build, the third figure took nine pieces to build, and so on. When you repeated the activity with a different triangle and two different rhombuses, did the pattern hold? Or was it different?

Solicit student answers. Students should find the same pattern holds true. Start a chart that recaps what students have found.

When the sides are this many times as long . . .	The area is this many times as large . . .
2	4
3	9
4	
5	
6	

Have students volunteer answers and complete the chart. Ask students to share with a partner their answers to Questions 7 and 8 (predicting the number of pieces to build the tenth square B and the tenth triangle N) on *Student Activity Book* page 49. After students have had time to discuss their ideas, ask for volunteers to share their answers.

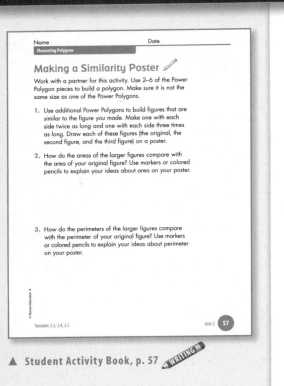

▲ **Student Activity Book, p. 57** WRITING

Student explanations are likely to include numeric and geometric reasoning. For example:

[Yumiko] says that she noticed a pattern of square numbers. So the tenth figure would take 10 times 10, or 100, pieces. What do people think? Do you agree with [Yumiko]? How could you use [Yumiko]'s explanation to describe what the tenth triangle N would look like?

[Tavon] says that he was thinking about what the shape would look like. To build the tenth square B, you'd have to start with ten squares across the bottom row, and you'd need ten rows. So the dimensions would be 10 by 10. Do you agree?

Ask students to continue thinking about these relationships as they continue their work in Math Workshop.

So we've been able to generalize that the area increases in the same way for polygons with three and four sides. You've been working with hexagons; do you think it will be true for hexagons as well? Why do you think so?

Solicit student answers. At this point, some students will be convinced by the patterns they have found for the polygons, while other students will remain unconvinced, arguing that so far they have only worked with three- or four-sided shapes, and have not yet finished the work with hexagons.

MATH WORKSHOP

45 MIN

Similar Polygons

Students continue working in the Math Workshop. Make them aware that their answers on *Student Activity Book* pages 53–54 will be discussed at the beginning of the next session, and that the similarity posters are due at the end of the next session.

Introduce the similarity poster.

Today, we're going to continue working in the Math Workshop, and there's also a new activity. You are going to work with a partner and use some combination of Power Polygon pieces to make a polygon. Then, you'll build similar shapes with sides two times and three times as long. You'll make a "Similarity Poster" showing the similar figures, and how the perimeter and area of these figures have increased.

Direct students' attention to *Student Activity Book* page 57, and answer any questions they might have about the activity.

2A Building Similar Hexagons

For complete details, see Session 3.2, pages 115–116, 120–122.

2B *LogoPaths* Activity: *Polygon Pairs* (optional)

For complete details, see Session 3.2, pages 116–119, 122–123.

2C Making a Similarity Poster

Have students work in pairs on *Student Activity Book* page 57. Students build a shape that is not a familiar polygon. They then use additional Power Polygon pieces to make larger shapes that are mathematically similar to their original shape. They make one with each side twice as long and another with each side three times as long as the original. ❶

To display their work as a poster, have students trace around their original shapes and the two similar shapes on large sheets of paper. If multiples of the whole original shape are used to make a similar shape, the student should draw a dark outline around the original shape anywhere it appears in the new shape. (See the first example in the **Teacher Note** on page 153.) Students can color-code their work by using one color to draw every identical piece.

A student works to create his similarity poster.

Once the poster is made, the student pairs investigate whether their similar polygons follow the generalizations they discovered earlier about the way area changes as perimeter changes. They label side lengths and areas. ❷

Professional Development

❶ **Teacher Note:** Building Larger Similar Figures, p. 153

Teaching Note

❷ **Labeling Sides and Area on Similarity Posters** Because some of the Power Polygon pieces have lengths that are not rational numbers (e.g., the hypotenuse of triangle D has a length of approximately $\sqrt{98}$ cm or $\sqrt{15}$ inches), students have to determine some way to label sides and areas in comparison to the original figure. One possibility is to show how each piece in the similar figure has side lengths two times the original and an area four times the original, as shown in the poster below.

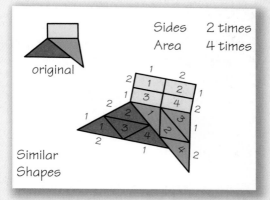

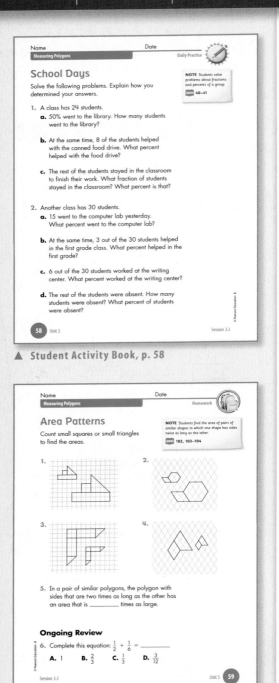

▲ Student Activity Book, p. 58

▲ Student Activity Book, p. 59

ONGOING ASSESSMENT: Observing Students at Work

Students create a similarity poster using a nonfamiliar polygon.

- **How do students build the similar shapes?** Are they able to use the entire shape to create a similar figure? Or do they have to use four or nine of each individual piece to create the similar figure? How do students know the shapes are similar?

- **Are students able to determine how the area changes?** How do they do this?

To help students build the similar figures, and consider perimeter and area of the figures, ask questions such as:

- How do you know your [second or third] shape is similar to the original? Are the angles the same? Are the sides [two or three] times longer? How do you know?

- What is the increase in area in the [second or third] figure? What is the increase in the perimeter in the [second or third] figure? How did you figure it out?

DIFFERENTIATION: Supporting the Range of Learners

Intervention Some students will benefit from using only two or three of the Power Polygon pieces and making a more familiar shape, such as a "long, skinny" parallelogram, or a right angle trapezoid.

Extension Other students can be challenged to create shapes that are smaller than the original shape, or to use larger pieces to make similar shapes (rather than just using four of each of the original shapes to create the larger similar shapes.)

SESSION FOLLOW-UP

3 ## Daily Practice and Homework

 Daily Practice: For ongoing review, have students complete *Student Activity Book* page 58.

 Homework: On *Student Activity Book* page 59, students find the area of pairs of similar shapes in which one shape in each pair has sides twice as long as the other.

 Student Math Handbook: Students and families may use *Student Math Handbook* pages 102, 103–104 for reference and review. See pages 170–173 in the back of this unit.

Similarity Posters

Math Focus Points

◆ Examining the relationship among angles, line lengths, and areas of similar polygons

◆ Building similar figures for polygons made from two or more Power Polygon pieces

◆ Using Power Polygons to find the areas of similar hexagons

Today's Plan		Materials
① DISCUSSION **Similar Hexagons** 15 MIN CLASS		• *Student Activity Book,* pp. 53–54 (from Session 3.2)
② MATH WORKSHOP **Similar Polygons** **2A** *LogoPaths* Activity: *Polygon Pairs* (optional) **2B** Making a Similarity Poster 45 MIN		**2A** • M4 (from Session 3.2) • Computers with *LogoPaths* software installed **2B** • *Student Activity Book,* p. 57 (from Session 3.3) • Power Polygons (2 sets, distributed evenly among groups of 3 or 4 students); chart paper; markers; colored pencils; crayons
③ SESSION FOLLOW-UP **Daily Practice and Homework**		• *Student Activity Book,* pp. 61–62 • *Student Math Handbook,* pp. 103–104.

Ten-Minute Math

Quick Survey For the survey, ask the class "What is your favorite pet—dog, cat, fish, hamster, or bird?" or a different categorical question that you or the students choose.

Make sure they collect data about something they already know or can observe easily.

With today's data set, make a bar graph. Ask students:

- What do you notice about the data?
- What do the data tell us about our class?

Math Note

❶ **Discussing the area of similar hexagons** The relationship that students noticed between side length and area of squares, rectangles, and triangles continues with other polygons, in this case, hexagons. The similar figure made by doubling the side lengths has four times as much area, and the similar figure made by tripling the side lengths has nine times as much area. However, unlike the earlier shapes, the enlarged shapes of the hexagon do not break apart into four (or nine) exact copies of the original shape. Instead, the regions that form that area must be decomposed into smaller shapes that cover the same area. For example, while the second figure for hexagon H cannot be made of four hexagon Hs, the area of the Power Polygon pieces used to create the second hexagon figure is equivalent to four of hexagon H.

DISCUSSION

① Similar Hexagons

Math Focus Points for Discussion

◆ Using Power Polygons to find the areas of similar hexagons

Ask students for different ways they made the second and third hexagon figures. Record some different combinations for each figure on the board or overhead. ❶

2nd Hexagon Figure				3rd Hexagon Figure			
Piece:	Number of pieces Alex	Number of pieces Shandra	Number of pieces Renaldo	Piece:	Number of pieces Hana	Number of pieces Cecilia	Number of pieces Talisha
triangle N		6	24	triangle N	6		54
rhombus M		6		rhombus M	12	6	
trapezoid K	6			trapezoid K	6	12	
hexagon H	1	1		hexagon H	1	1	

Ask for volunteers to explain how they determined the area, in hexagons, of each of the figures.

Students might say:

"For my second one, I used one hexagon and six trapezoids. Since two trapezoids make one hexagon, six trapezoids make three hexagons, so the area would be four hexagons all together."

"I used the same idea. I used six triangles— that's one hexagon. I used six of the rhombuses. It takes three of the rhombuses to make one hexagon, so six would be two hexagons. So I have three hexagons, plus the one, so it's four."

"I just made the whole thing out of triangles, and it took 24. I know six triangles make one hexagon, so 24 ÷ 6 = 4. So it's four hexagons."

Give students the opportunity to question each other and to explain their solutions. Establish that the second figure would have an area four times greater than the original hexagon, and the third figure would have an area nine times greater. Ask students to consider any polygon.

Is everyone convinced that the same pattern we've been seeing still holds? That if you increase each side of a polygon by two, the area increases by four? Or if we increase each side by three, the area increases by nine? For how many shapes have we found this to be true?

Solicit student responses—they should include not only the Power Polygon pieces from this Investigation, but also the squares and rectangles from Investigation 2. If necessary, remind students of their work with squares and rectangles.

Do you think this will always be true?

Give students a minute or two to discuss this with a partner, and then collect student responses.

[Mitch] says that we still haven't tried every shape. He originally didn't think it would work for a hexagon because of its shape, but it did. It is also turning out to be true so far on his similarity poster. So he's beginning to think it might always be true, no matter what the polygon. Any thoughts?❷

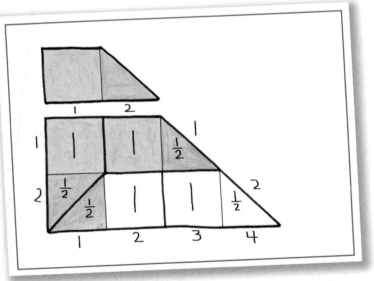

Mitch's work

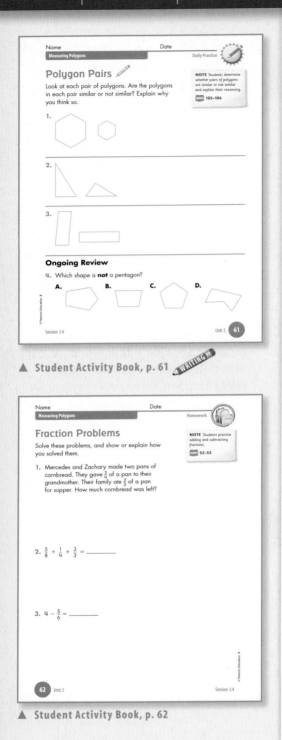

▲ Student Activity Book, p. 61

▲ Student Activity Book, p. 62

MATH WORKSHOP

45 MIN

② Similar Polygons

Students complete their similarity posters and continue to determine whether pairs of polygons are similar in the *LogoPaths* activity, *Polygon Pairs*. Those students who have completed pairs 1–8 can move on to the next set of *Polygon Pairs*.

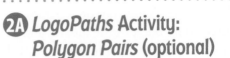
PAIRS INDIVIDUALS

②A *LogoPaths* Activity: *Polygon Pairs* (optional)

For complete details about this activity, see Session 3.2, pages 116–119, 122–123.

②B Making a Similarity Poster

PAIRS

Students work in pairs to complete their similarity posters and answer the questions on *Student Activity Book* page 57. Similarity posters are discussed in the next session after students complete the End-of-Unit Assessment.

For complete details about this activity, see Session 3.3, pages 127–128.

SESSION FOLLOW-UP

③ Daily Practice and Homework

Daily Practice: For reinforcement of this unit's content, have students complete *Student Activity Book* page 61.

Homework: Students solve addition and subtraction problems involving fractions on *Student Activity Book* page 62.

Student Math Handbook: Students and families may use *Student Math Handbook* pages 103–104 for reference and review. See pages 170–173 in the back of this unit.

End-of-Unit Assessment

Math Focus Points

- Using known angles to find the measures of other angles
- Creating different rectangles with the same perimeter but different areas
- Recognizing and building similar figures

Today's Plan		Materials
ASSESSMENT ACTIVITY **❶ End-of-Unit Assessment**	✓ 🕐 👤 20 MIN INDIVIDUALS	• M20–M22*
ACTIVITY **❷ Similarity Posters**	🕐 👥 👥 40 MIN GROUPS PAIRS	• Similarity posters (from Sessions 3.3 and 3.4)
SESSION FOLLOW-UP **❸ Daily Practice**		• *Student Activity Book*, p. 63 • *Student Math Handbook*, pp. 103–104

*See *Materials to Prepare*, p. 107.

Ten-Minute Math

Quick Survey For the survey, ask the class "How many pockets are you wearing today?" or a different numerical question that you or the students choose. Make sure they collect data about something they already know or can observe easily. With today's data set, make a line plot. Ask students:

- What do you notice about the data?
- What do the data tell us about our class?

Professional Development

1 Teacher Note: End-of-Unit Assessment, p. 155

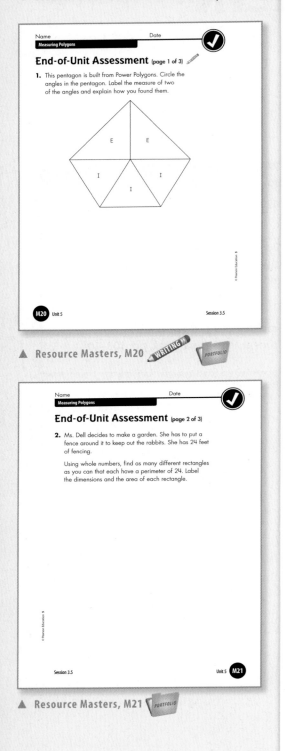

▲ Resource Masters, M20

▲ Resource Masters, M21

ASSESSMENT ACTIVITY

1 End-of-Unit Assessment

20 MIN   INDIVIDUALS

On End-of-Unit Assessment (M20–M22), students work individually to solve three problems designed to assess three of the unit's benchmarks. **1**

In Problem 1 students find angle measures in a figure made from Power Polygons. This problem addresses Benchmark 2, which uses known angle sizes to determine the sizes of other angles (30°, 45°, 90°, and 150°). In Problem 2 students find the dimensions and areas of rectangles with the same perimeter. This problem addresses Benchmark 3, which determines the perimeter and area of rectangles. In Problem 3 students determine whether two polygons are similar. This problem addresses Benchmark 4, which identifies mathematically similar polygons.

As students finish the assessment, allow them to work quietly with a partner to complete their similarity posters.

ONGOING ASSESSMENT: Observing Students at Work

Students identify and find the measure of angles in a pentagon, create rectangles with the same perimeter but different areas, and identify and draw similar rectangles.

- **Are students able to identify the five angles of the pentagon?**

- **How do students find the size of the angles in the pentagon?** Do they recognize and use "landmark" angles, such as 90°, 45°, and 60°?

- **How do students create different rectangles with a perimeter of 24 feet?** Do they use trial and error, or do they use a more systematic approach, such as finding dimensions that sum to 12, or using the same number to increase one dimension and decrease the other?

- **How do students decide whether the two rectangles are similar?** Are they able to correctly draw a similar rectangle?

DIFFERENTIATION: Supporting the Range of Learners

Intervention Allow students to use any material needed, such as Power Polygon pieces, grid paper, or square tiles. For Problem 3, if students are having problems writing about similarity, have them first explain it to you and then have them write their response.

ACTIVITY
2 Similarity Posters

40 MIN GROUPS PAIRS

Allow students time to make sure their similarity posters are completed. Place students into groups of six to eight members so they may examine a collection of three or four posters. Student pairs explain to their small groups how they know the enlarged figures are similar to their original, and also explain what they found out about the perimeter and the area. Students check one another's posters and make suggestions for showing their findings on the posters. If necessary, students help one another determine how many of the original sides and areas fit into each similar shape. Once the posters are reviewed, they should be displayed around the classroom.

As you circulate among the groups, focus the conversation on how the poster illustrates students' observations. For example:

The way this poster is shaded helps me to see the way each Power Polygon on the original shape is used four times in the larger figure.

The way you have the perimeter marked on this poster helps me see how you know each side increases by two. What I think you're showing is that if the perimeter of each Power Polygon piece in the original figure is increased by two, then that means the perimeter of the whole second similar figure is increased by two.

SESSION FOLLOW-UP
3 Daily Practice

Daily Practice: For enrichment, have students complete *Student Activity Book* page 63.

Student Math Handbook: Students and families may use *Student Math Handbook* pages 103–104 for reference and review. See pages 170–173 in the back of this unit.

Name _____ Date _____
Measuring Polygons

End-of-Unit Assessment (page 3 of 3)

3. Consider the following rectangles:

Rectangle A   Rectangle B

A. Are the two rectangles similar? Explain why you think so.

B. If you do not think they are similar, draw a rectangle that is similar to rectangle A.

M22 Unit 5   Session 3.5

▲ Resource Masters, M22 WRITING PORTFOLIO

Name _____ Date _____
Measuring Polygons   Daily Practice

Similar Polygons

B
A ☐ C
D

NOTE Students determine dimension for polygons that are similar by creating a table, and then explain their reasoning.
SMH 103–104

Austin is choosing a pool for his backyard. He has found a design that he likes in the brochure. Austin wants a pool that is similar, but he will enlarge the dimensions to double the size of the pool he chose in the brochure.

1. Use the table to determine the dimensions of his pool. Each side of the pool is doubled. Write the new dimensions for each side in the table.

	Side A	Side B	Side C	Side D
Austin's Pool				
Brochure Pool	4 ft	8 ft	4 ft	8 ft

2. Draw a picture of Austin's pool. Label the dimensions of each side of the pool.

3. Explain why the two pools are similar.

Session 3.5   Unit 5 63

▲ Student Activity Book, p. 63

Measuring Polygons

In Part 6 of *Implementing Investigations in Grade 5,* you will find a set of Teacher Notes that addresses topics and issues applicable to the curriculum as a whole rather than to specific curriculum units. They include the following:

Computational Fluency and Place Value

Computational Algorithms and Methods

Representations and Contexts for Mathematical Work

Foundations of Algebra in the Elementary Grades

Discussing Mathematical Ideas

Racial and Linguistic Diversity in the Classroom:
   What Does Equity Mean in Today's Math Classroom?

Classification of Triangles and Quadrilaterals

Classification systems help people organize information about the world into categories. Sometimes these categories are hierarchical, and sometimes they are also overlapping. For example, a person might live in the city of Cleveland, which is in the state of Ohio, which is in the United States, which is in North America. If you know someone who lives in Cleveland, you also know that that person lives in Ohio, in the United States, and in North America. In fact, everyone who lives in Cleveland also lives in Ohio, and so on. However, one cannot make the same kind of assumptions in reverse; it is not true that everyone who lives in Ohio lives in Cleveland. This is an example of hierarchical classification.

Mathematicians use a hierarchical classification system to sort geometric figures. The activities in this unit help clarify the classification of triangles and quadrilaterals.

Triangles

There are two ways to classify triangles: by their angles and by their sides. Classified by their angles, triangles are right (one 90° angle), acute (all angles less than 90°), or obtuse (one angle greater than 90°). These categories are illustrated by the horizontal loops in the diagram. Classified by their sides, triangles are scalene (no sides the same length), isosceles (at least two sides the same length), or equilateral (all sides the same length).

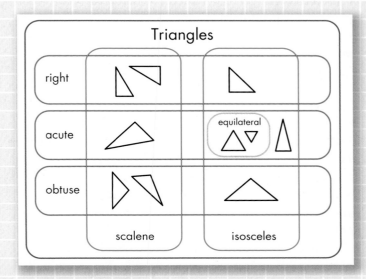

Consider two triangles:

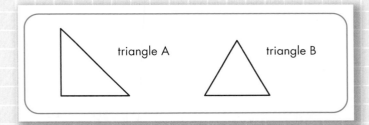

Triangle A has two sides the same length and a 90° angle, so it is both right and isosceles: a right isosceles triangle. Part of the work in Grade 5 helps students understand that a single figure may belong to more than one category.

There are also more complex relationships: triangle B is acute (because it has three acute angles), equilateral (because it has three equal sides), and isosceles (because at least two of its sides are equal). That is why it lies inside three loops. So, triangle B is an equilateral triangle. It is also isosceles, a triangle, and a polygon, as are all equilateral triangles.

To help students keep track of the attributes of each of these classifications, it is helpful to speak of an object by its most restrictive category. For example, if a triangle has three equal sides, it is called equilateral rather than isosceles or just a triangle. To help students visualize these attributes, however, it is helpful for them to see the least restrictive examples. In this case, an isosceles triangle is drawn with two equal sides, not three, and a general triangle is drawn as a scalene triangle without a right angle.

Quadrilaterals

Quadrilaterals are classified by their sides and their angles. In considering sides, the characteristics to pay attention to are the length of the sides and whether pairs of sides are parallel. For example, trapezoids have exactly one pair of parallel sides that are not equal in length, and opposite nonparallel sides may or may not be equal in length. If one pair of opposite sides in a trapezoid is equal in length, the figure is called an isosceles trapezoid, the trapezoid that is most familiar to fifth graders. A trapezoid can be further classified by whether or not it contains a right angle.

Parallelograms have two pairs of parallel sides and opposite sides that are equal in length. Rhombuses (or rhombi) are members of the parallelogram family that have all four sides equal. Rectangles are also members of the parallelogram family. The angles are what make rectangles special; all four angles are equal and measure 90°. Squares are in many families, including rectangle (because the angles are all the same size), rhombus (because the sides are all the same length), and parallelogram (because there are two pairs of parallel sides).

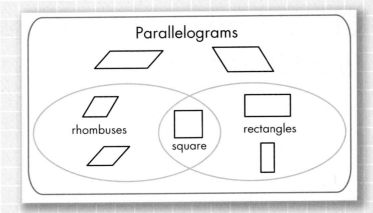

Other kinds of quadrilaterals do not fit into the categories of either trapezoids or parallelograms because they do not have any parallel sides. These quadrilaterals may, however, have some sides that are equal in length, such as the first two examples in the figure below. Quadrilaterals may have angles that are four different sizes, as in the second two examples below. They may also have an angle that is greater than 180°, which makes a concave quadrilateral, as in the last two examples.

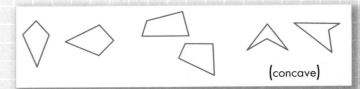

Such a traditional classification is just one useful way to sort geometric figures. One could just as well declare that rectangles cannot have all equal sides, thereby excluding squares from the family of rectangles. Students often initially prefer this partitioning way of classifying. Only with time do they come to see the advantages of hierarchical classification—for example, if you know a square is a rectangle, then you know that it has all of the properties of rectangles. The important emphases for students at this stage are to be able to identify the attributes of the different types of quadrilaterals and to understand that some quadrilaterals can be classified in more than one way.

Introducing and Managing the *LogoPaths* Software

The use of computer activities is optional in this unit. However, if computers are available, it is recommended that you use the software. The geometry software activities extend and deepen the mathematical ideas that are emphasized in this unit. The software activities allow students to work with geometric shapes and angles in ways that are not possible in regular classroom activities.

Activities with the *LogoPaths* software are suggested throughout each investigation in this unit. First, you will need to consider how you will introduce your students to the *LogoPaths* software. Then, you will need to consider how students will have access to this software. You may introduce each new software activity to the whole class if you have access to a large screen projection setup. If you have access to a computer lab, consider introducing each new activity to the whole class in this environment. If your school has a computer teacher, consider collaborating with that teacher to have students work on these activities during some of their scheduled time in the computer lab. In this unit the activities are included as Math Workshop activities; once students are introduced to an activity, they can then access the activity during Math Workshops.

Regardless of the number of computers you have, students generally benefit by working on these activities in pairs. This not only maximizes computer resources, but also encourages students to consult, monitor, and teach one another. Each pair should spend at least 15–20 minutes at the computer for each activity.

Introducing the *LogoPaths* Software

Computer Lab If you have a computer laboratory with one computer for each pair of students, all of your students can be introduced to and become familiar with the computer activities at the same time. In this situation, you will not need to devote time during math class for introducing students to the new software activity.

Large Screen Monitor or Projection Screen If you have access to either of these devices, you can introduce the software activities to the whole class during the math session immediately before Math Workshop or at another time of the day.

Small Groups of Students You can introduce the software activities to small groups of students either before or during Math Workshop. These students can then be paired with other students and become "teachers" of the software.

Managing the Computer Environment

Math Workshop Students should have access to the *LogoPaths* software consistently throughout the unit. If you have daily access to a computer lab, you might choose to add this experience to your day in addition to your regular math class. Typically classrooms have a limited number of computers. While three to five computers is ideal, students can have a successful computer experience with only one to two. In the case of fewer computers, you will need to incorporate additional computer time for students throughout the day. If you have computers available in your classroom, pairs of students can cycle through the computer activities, just as they cycle through the other Math Workshop activities.

Using *LogoPaths* All Year This is the only unit in the Grade 5 sequence that explicitly suggests activities to go with the sessions in the unit. However, it is strongly recommended that students use the software throughout the year. Earlier units include suggestions of *LogoPaths* activities that students were introduced to in Grade 4, and later units include suggestions and Teacher Resources for activities that students can continue for the remainder of the school year. With experience, students become increasingly fluent in the mechanics of the software itself and can better focus on the mathematical ideas of the games and activities. They should continue to explore the games that develop understanding of paths and turning angles, as well as the Free Explore activities that focus on the properties of 2-D shapes, including their angles.

Introducing the *LogoPaths* Software

In your first introduction of *Angle and Turn,* show students the following:

- How to open *Angle and Turn* by clicking on it once

- How to enter right and left turn commands in degrees of any amount (e.g., **RT 50 LF 110**)

- How to use the **Turtle Turner** tool

In your first introduction of the *Triangles* and *Rhombuses and Parallelograms* activities, show students the following:

- How to open *Free Explore* by clicking on it once

- How to enter forward and backward commands in the Command Center (e.g., **FD 82 BK 125**)

- How to enter right and left turn commands in degrees of any amount (e.g., **RT 50 LT 110**). Note that both move and turn input must be between −999 and 999.

- How to delete a command they wish to change

- How to use the **Label Lengths** and **Label Turns** tools

- How to use the **Turtle Turner** and **Ruler** tools

- How to use the **Teach Tool** to make a procedure out of a set of commands in the Command Center. You will be asked to give it a name and the commands will be moved to the Teach Window in the proper format for a procedure.

In your first introduction of the *Polygon Pairs* activity, show students the following:

- How to open *Polygon Pairs* by clicking on it once

- How to pick a specific *Polygon Pairs* puzzle

- How to use the **Label Lengths** and **Label Turns** tools to compare the polygons within each pair

- How to use the **Overlay** procedures to compare the polygons within each pair

You can introduce more of the tools available in *LogoPaths* as students indicate interest and the need to use them.

- Students can use the penup (**PU**) and pendown (**PD**) commands to tell the turtle whether to draw as it moves. Type **PU** in the Command Center to move without drawing. Type **PD** for the turtle to draw as it moves.

- The repeat command tells the turtle to repeat a set of commands a specified number of times. The first input is the number of times to repeat, and the second is a list of commands enclosed in square brackets. For example, to repeat a forward move and a right turn three times, students might type **REPEAT 3 [FD 100 RT 90]**.

- You can hide the turtle by typing **HT**. Type **ST** in the Command Center to see the turtle again.

- Students can change the color, shape and size of the turtle and the line it draws using the Turtle features panel. Other features of how the turtle works (e.g., its speed) can be changed in the Preferences panel.

- Further information about commands, tools and buttons can be found in the online Help.

It is likely that many students will discover other tools and their uses on their own as they spend more time working with the software. Encourage them to share their discoveries with each other.

Saving Student Work

If you want to discuss students' work later, have them either print it or save it to a disk. For more information, refer to the *Software Support Guide* found on the software CD.

About the Mathematics in the *LogoPaths* Software

The *LogoPaths* software provides an environment in which students can explore geometry, patterns, logical thinking, and more. The essential metaphor in Logo is "playing turtle"—taking the perspective of the turtle (the drawing cursor) to move and turn to make shapes and designs. This is a very natural view of geometry for children because it matches how individuals explore the world—through questions such as "How much farther do I need to move?" and "Which way should I turn to get to a particular place?"

When they use *LogoPaths,* students explore a number of geometric and other mathematical ideas. This includes explicit investigation of length and perimeter and the equality of lengths of opposite sides in a parallelogram. It also includes exploration of the sizes of angles and the relationship between the turning (or exterior) angle and the interior angle of polygons. *LogoPaths* is another context in which students come to see a variety of representations of numerical ideas—bigger or smaller means a different thing with respect to length, angle, number of sides, etc.

Using the *LogoPaths* software in Grades 3 through 5 also allows students to explore many kinds of patterns and relationships. For example, they discover that the first two sides of a rectangle always have half the total perimeter; that consecutive sides of a parallelogram have turning angles that total 180°; that a polygon with only 90 degree turns always has an even number of sides; and that the turning (exterior) angles in a polygon total 360 degrees (which means that the turning angle in a regular polygon is always 360 divided by the number of sides). You can encourage students to look for a wide variety of patterns and see whether they can explain when they are true and why. Creating procedures with variable inputs is another way of focusing on regularities and patterns; such procedures define a whole class of shapes with the same structure but with different sizes, angles, etc.

LogoPaths offers students a chance to see a variety of inverse operations—that is, pairs of commands that undo one another's effects. For example, moving forward and then back the same amount leaves the turtle in the same place. Other inverse operations include right and left, penup and pendown, and hide turtle and show turtle. Students can also explore arithmetic inverses with addition and subtraction, multiplication and division, or positive and negative numbers. *LogoPaths* allows students to pair the concept of an inverse with a visual component.

Students also learn careful logical thinking by working with *LogoPaths.* Because the turtle only does exactly what students tell it to do, students learn to be precise in their instructions. If the turtle does something unexpected, students learn to break down the instructions step by step; by "playing turtle" to figure out just how their instructions led to this unexpected behavior, students can deduce how to change that behavior. Some of *LogoPaths'* debugging tools (e.g., the Stop tool, the Step tool, and highlighting of steps, even through procedures in the Teach window) can help in this process. (The Software Support Reference guide and the online Help text provide more information about these tools.) By making procedures that can be used by other procedures, students also break down complex ideas and projects into smaller, more manageable chunks. For example, a procedure to make a house might move the turtle to the right positions and then use a square procedure for windows, a rectangle procedure for the door, and a triangle procedure for the roof. These sorts of logical and analytical problem-solving approaches are important to mathematical thinking.

The Rule of 180°

Understanding angles and angle measures is critical to understanding geometric shapes like triangles and squares. Turtle turning is a powerful and dynamic way to learn about these concepts.

When students use the *LogoPaths* software, they need to understand the relationship between the angle that the turtle turns and the angle that is formed between the lines the turtle draws before and after it turns. For example, the figure below shows the turtle's position after starting on the left and moving forward 100 steps toward the right.

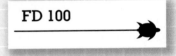

The next figure shows the position of the turtle and the new direction it faces after it turns 120°.

Below are the results of the turtle moving forward 100 steps in the new direction.

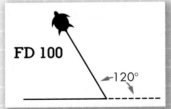

Note that when the turtle moves forward after turning, the angle between the lines the turtle draws before and after it turns is a 60° angle. Even though the turtle has turned through 120°, the lines it draws form a 60° angle.

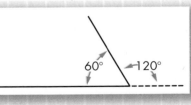

Notice that with 90° turns, the amount the turtle turns and the measure of the drawn angle are the same:

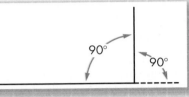

Some students mix up the turning angle, or exterior angle, and the angle that is formed, or interior angle. Keep checking to see that students are visualizing and correctly representing the angle through which the turtle turns (120° in the first set of figures to the left), and the angle that is formed (60° in the second set). It is useful to reinforce that the greater the turn or exterior angle, the smaller the interior angle.

Another common confusion for students is the relationship of the length of the sides to the measure of the angle. Many students think that a larger angle is one with longer sides, or more "area." Thus they believe that of the three angles pictured here, angle B is the largest and angle C is the smallest.

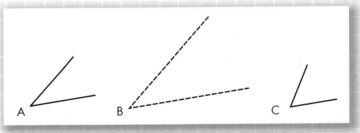

Remind students that the measure of an angle is the amount of turn from one side to the other. Superimposing pairs of angles shows that angles A and B actually have the same measure, and angle C has a greater measure than angle B.

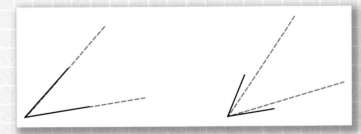

Assessment: Quadrilaterals and Angles

Problem 1

Benchmark addressed:

Benchmark 1: Identify different quadrilaterals by attribute, and know that some quadrilaterals can be classified in more than one way.

In order to meet the benchmark, students' work should show that they can:

- Correctly identify the figure by each of the three terms (square, rhombus, and parallelogram), and know that all three apply;

- Include at least the following attributes in their explanations:

  —A square and a rhombus both have 4 equal sides;

  —A square, a rhombus, and a parallelogram all have two pairs of parallel sides.

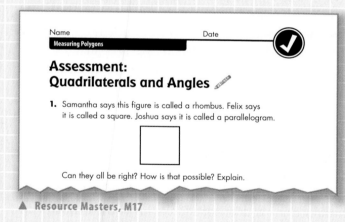

Name   Date

Measuring Polygons

Assessment:
Quadrilaterals and Angles

1. Samantha says this figure is called a rhombus. Felix says it is called a square. Joshua says it is called a parallelogram.

Can they all be right? How is that possible? Explain.

▲ **Resource Masters, M17**

As you look at student work for this problem, keep in mind that a response that meets the benchmark must include at least the above information. However, some students may include more than that, such as describing all the attributes of each type of quadrilateral. On the other hand, many students may not be explicit about what makes the figure a square; at this point, you can expect that fifth graders "just know" this from looking at the figure.

Meeting the Benchmark

Students who meet the benchmark identify the figure as a rhombus, a square, and a parallelogram. Their explanation includes that it is both a rhombus and a square because it has four equal sides, and that it is also a parallelogram because it has two sets of parallel sides.

Alicia recognizes the figure as a square and clearly states that a square is both a "kind" of rhombus and a "kind" of parallelogram. She includes the attributes that squares share with both of these quadrilateral types (four equal sides that are parallel) in her explanation.

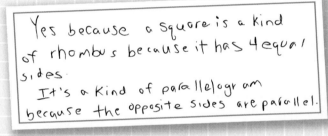

Yes because a square is a kind of rhombus because it has 4 equal sides.
It's a kind of parallelogram because the opposite sides are parallel.

Alicia's Work

Zachary responded to the question by stating that each student is right and listing the attributes of each term.

rhombus— yes, 4 equal sides
square — yes, 4 equal sides and 4 right angles
parallelogram yes a sets of parallel lines, like this ═ ‖

Zachary's Work

Partially Meeting the Benchmark

Students who partially meet the benchmark recognize that the terms *square, rhombus,* and *parallelogram* all apply to the figure, and demonstrate they understand that one figure can be described by more than one term. However, their explanations may not include describing the attributes which make the figure fit each category.

For example, Georgia knows that a square and rhombus have attributes in common, but she does not state what they are. She does include the attribute of having parallel sides.

> a square is like a rhombus only it's just slanted differently. It also has parallel lines so it's like a parallelogram, too.

Georgia's Work

Avery uses visual references for identifying the figure as both a square and a rhombus, rather than stating what attribute the two types of quadrilaterals share. He does include the attribute of having parallel sides.

> I know it's a square because it looks like a square.
> The way it's made is like how a rhombus is made.
> Everything is parallel from the other.

Avery's Work

Lourdes is able to say that the figure is both a square and a rhombus, and can explain why. However, her definition of parallelogram is incorrect; just as she visualizes a rhombus as a "tilted" square, she also believes that a parallelogram is a "tilted rectangle," and therefore cannot be a square. Lourdes's answer suggests that she may not be clear that a square is also a rectangle.

> It's a square and a rhombus because they both have equal sides. A rhombus just has a little tilt. It can't be a parallelogram because that's like a tilted rectangle.

Lourdes's Work

Students who offer responses like these should be questioned and asked to explain their thinking further. Do they in fact know that what makes a square a rhombus is that a rhombus is any quadrilateral with four equal sides? Do they know that a parallelogram has exactly two pairs of opposite sides that are parallel? If some students are unclear about these descriptions, have them review the appropriate pages in the *Student Math Handbook*. They may also benefit from continuing to categorize quadrilaterals as they play *Guess My Rule*.

Not Meeting the Benchmark

Students do not meet the benchmark if their responses either include some information that is incorrect (such as that the figure is only a square), or if they offer a statement that is generally true but does not address any of the attributes that these types of quadrilaterals have in common.

Stuart makes a very general statement, which is essentially that all three shapes (square, rhombus, and parallelogram) are quadrilaterals. He does not address the question of how the figure shown can be described by each of the three terms.

> *It's all three things because they all have four sides.*

Stuart's Work

Make a note of students who are not yet clear about the attributes of each of the types of quadrilaterals, who have incorrect notions about what defines a particular quadrilateral, or who are still convinced that each quadrilateral type is an exclusive category. For instance, some students may still believe that a square can only be a square, not a rectangle, or that a rhombus is different from a square because it does not have right angles. Direct students who are still having difficulty to spend more time reviewing, identifying, and classifying a variety of quadrilaterals using both the Shape Cards and the Power Polygons.

Problem 2

Benchmark addressed:

Benchmark 2: Use known angle sizes to determine the sizes of other angles (30 degrees, 45 degrees, 60 degrees, 90 degrees, 120 degrees, and 150 degrees).

In order to meet the benchmarks, students' work should show that they can:

- Identify each of the four angles in the quadrilateral;
- Recognize a 90° angle;
- Accurately find the measure of each of the other three angles created by combining two smaller angles.

2. Look at the quadrilateral below that was made from Power Polygons. Circle the four angles in this quadrilateral. Use the Power Polygon pieces to find the size of each angle. Label the size of each angle and explain how you know.

Session 1.7 Unit 5 **M17**

▲ **Resource Masters, M17**

It is expected that most students will continue to use the Power Polygon pieces as reference for finding the measure of the angles in this new polygon. At this point, some students may have enough experience with the measures of some of the Power Polygon angles that they can now use these as "benchmark" angles. For instance, they may know that an equilateral triangle has three 60° angles or that an isosceles right triangle has two 45° angles, and therefore they would not need to explain these measures each time they use them.

Meeting the Benchmark

Students who meet the benchmark can identify and accurately find the measure of each of the four angles in the quadrilateral. Their explanations include what references they used to find the measures (such as Power Polygon pieces), and how they combined angle measures to find the size of angles that do not match any of the Power Polygon pieces exactly.

Charles used what he knew about the size of the angles in the Power Polygon pieces that make up the quadrilateral. He accurately combined these angle sizes to find the measure of the angles in the quadrilateral.

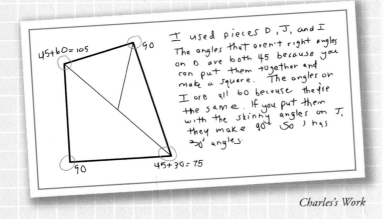

I used pieces D, J, and I
The angles that aren't right angles on D are both 45 because you can put them together and make a square. The angles on I are all 60 because they're the same. If you put them with the skinny angles on J, they make 90. So J has 30° angles.

45+60=105   90

90   45+30=75

Charles's Work

Olivia also used Power Polygon pieces that she recognized in the figure. However, instead of using the exact pieces, she saw the shape of another polygon (shape L) that was similar and knew that she could use those angle sizes as reference for finding these new angle measurements.

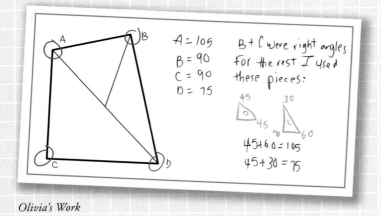

A = 105   B + C were right angles
B = 90   for the rest I used
C = 90   these pieces:
D = 75

45   30
D 45   L 60
90
45+60=105
45+30=75

Olivia's Work

Martin knew the size of all the angles in the polygons that make up the quadrilateral. His notation shows that he was clear about which angles he needed to combine in order to get the measures of the angles of the quadrilaterals.

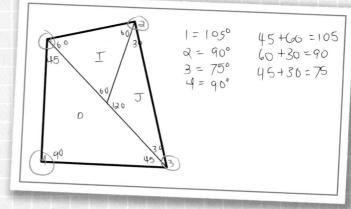

1 = 105°   45+60 =105
2 = 90°   60+30 =90
3 = 75°   45+30 =75
4 = 90°

Martin's Work

Felix used one Power Polygon angle that he was familiar with (the 30° angle in shape O) as a reference for measuring all the angles in the quadrilateral. In doing so, he noticed that he could use just part of the measure of that angle to fill in what he calls the "leftover," and recognized this part as half of 30°, or 15°.

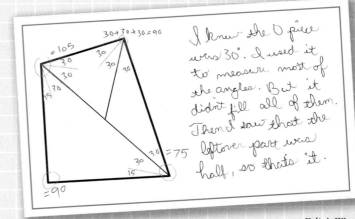

30+30+30=90
=105
30   30
30   30   30
30
15 30
45+30 =75
30
15
=90

I knew the O piece was 30°. I used it to measure most of the angles. But it didn't fill all of them. Then I saw that the leftover part was half, so that's it.

Felix's Work

Partially Meeting the Benchmark

Students who partially meet the benchmark demonstrate that they are able to identify the angles in the quadrilateral and find some angle measures on the Power Polygon pieces. However, they may not be carrying through with their strategies, or they may be relying on visual references rather than on the actual measures of the angles.

For example, Janet accurately found the measure of the polygon pieces that make up the quadrilateral, but she did not add these together to find the measure of the angles of the quadrilateral itself.

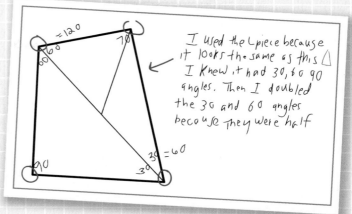

Tamira's Work

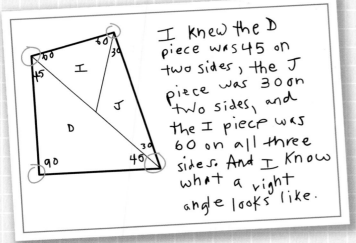

Janet's Work

Tamira recognized that she could use shape L as a reference for the three angles other than the right angle in the quadrilateral; she seems to already know the size of the angles in this polygon piece. However, she made an assumption that the diagonal line inside the quadrilateral bisects the two opposite angles, and therefore she doubled the angles in shape L to find the measure of those angles. She did not notice that the angle she labeled as 120° is not large enough to be twice the size of the angle she labeled as 60°.

Students like Janet and Tamira should be asked to look again at the whole angle and think about how they would find the total measure, not just the measures of the component parts. Ask questions such as "How do you know that angle measures 60°?" and have students consider whether or not their answers seem reasonable by comparing them to other angle measures they have found. They may also benefit from constructing other polygons from the Power Polygon pieces and finding some of the angle measures in those.

Not Meeting the Benchmark

Students who do not meet the benchmark are still unsure about how to use one angle measure to find the measure of another. They may be guessing, arbitrarily using angle measures they have heard mentioned, or unsure about which are the angles of the quadrilateral. Their knowledge of angle measures may still be limited to whether an angle is greater, less than, or equal to 90°, as is the case with Mitch.

Rather than using the different angles in the Power Polygons, Mitch used only the corner of his paper as a reference for 90°.

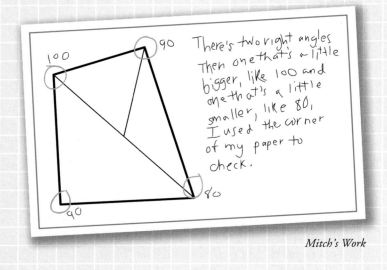

There's two right angles. Then one that's a little bigger, like 100 and one that's a little smaller, like 80. I used the corner of my paper to check.

Mitch's Work

For students who do not meet the benchmark, it is important to find what they do know in order to build from a starting place. With Mitch, for example, his starting place is being able to recognize whether or not an angle is larger or smaller than a right angle. His teacher may want to have him identify only acute angles in the Power Polygons and sort them according to which are the same size and which are different, repeating this procedure for the obtuse angles. Students like Mitch will need to spend more time identifying specific angle sizes, like 30° and 60°. Having students combine these angles in a variety of ways to create new angles will help them become familiar with a wider range of angle measures.

Assessment: Perimeter and Area of Rectangles

Benchmark addressed:

Benchmark 3: Find the perimeter and area of rectangles.

In order to meet the benchmark, students' work should show that they can:

- Distinguish between the measure of perimeter and area;

- Accurately find the perimeter and area of a rectangle;

- Create a rectangle with the same perimeter but a different area;

- Create a rectangle with the same area but a different perimeter.

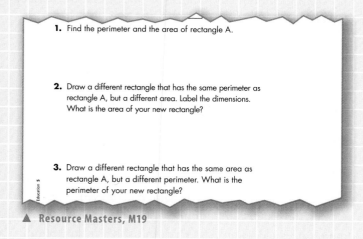

1. Find the perimeter and the area of rectangle A.

2. Draw a different rectangle that has the same perimeter as rectangle A, but a different area. Label the dimensions. What is the area of your new rectangle?

3. Draw a different rectangle that has the same area as rectangle A, but a different perimeter. What is the perimeter of your new rectangle?

▲ Resource Masters, M19

Meeting the Benchmark

Students who meet this benchmark understand what perimeter and area measure, and are able to use that knowledge to create new rectangles with either a different perimeter or a different area. To find a rectangle with the same perimeter, they create rectangles with dimensions that sum to ten. To find a rectangle with the same area, they use either factors of 24, or "cut and paste" the original rectangle.

To find the perimeter, Tamira adds the dimensions and multiplies the sum by 2. She then multiplies the dimensions to find the area. Tamira accurately finds a rectangle with the same perimeter and a rectangle with the same area, and could be challenged to find as many rectangles as possible with the same perimeter and area.

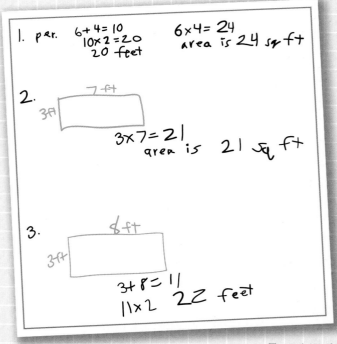

Tamira's Work

To find the perimeter in problem 1, Joshua draws grid lines and counts along each edge by ones to get the correct answer of 20. In problem 3, he adds up all of the side lengths to get the correct perimeter of 28. To find the area in the first two problems, Joshua draws grids in the rectangles, and skip counts to arrive at the correct answer. While he is not using multiplication to find the area and perimeter, as would be expected in Grade 5, he clearly can identify and find each measure. To create the rectangle in problem 3, Joshua "cuts and pastes" the first rectangle, and correctly labels each part of the new rectangle. While Joshua meets this benchmark, he needs support to more efficiently find perimeter and area.

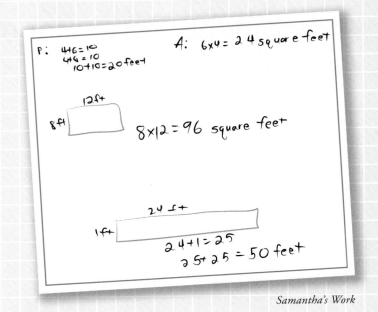

Samantha's Work

Martin confuses perimeter and area, which some students may continue to do. For problem 1, Martin has the correct answers, but he labels the perimeter as area, and vice versa. He is consistent with this mistake throughout the assessment. In problem 2, he draws a rectangle that actually is correct (a 5 by 5 square would have the same perimeter and different area), but he says his answer is the area, when it is actually the perimeter. In problem 3, he draws a rectangle that has the same perimeter and different area (instead of the same area) and incorrectly labels his answer as the perimeter. Martin does not label his area answers as square feet, which may indicate a misunderstanding about what area measures. He needs help remembering that perimeter is the distance around a shape, and that area is the amount of space an object covers, measured in square units.

Joshua's Work

Partially Meeting the Benchmark

Some students make computation errors in calculating perimeter and area measurements, confuse perimeter and area, or are unable to complete each of the questions.

Samantha correctly finds the perimeter and area of each of the rectangles. She adds to find the perimeter and multiplies to find the area. For problem 2, however, it seems likely Samantha makes a miscalculation—finding that two numbers that equal 20, instead of remembering perimeter includes all four sides—when she uses 8 and 12 as dimensions for her rectangle. Her teacher might ask Samantha what the perimeter of this rectangle (8 by 12) would be, and if that has the same perimeter as the rectangle in problem 1.

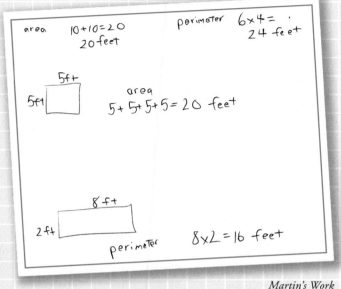

Martin's Work

Stuart is able to correctly find area by multiplying the dimensions. When finding perimeter, Stuart adds the two dimensions, not realizing this sum gives him only $\frac{1}{2}$ the perimeter. Ask students like Stuart what perimeter measures, and ask them to label every side of the rectangle. These students might also benefit from building rectangles with square tiles or drawing them on grid paper, and finding the perimeter.

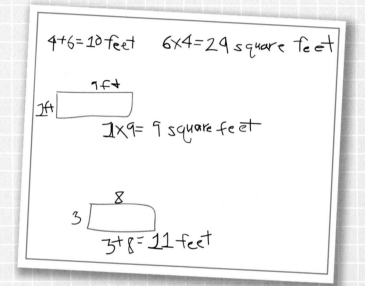

Stuart's Work

Some students are able to correctly answer problems 1 and 3 in this assessment, but are unable to find rectangles that have the same perimeter but a different area. These students benefit from doing more problems like "Fencing a Garden." Through trial and error, they begin to see that to find rectangles with the same perimeter, they need to find dimensions that have the same sum as the original rectangles.

Not Meeting the Benchmark

Most students are able to successfully complete this assessment. Some students, like Stuart, have an incomplete understanding of perimeter.

Teacher Note

Similar Shapes

In general usage, the word *similar* means having characteristics in common. In geometry, the word is more precise: Two figures are similar if they have exactly the same shape—if their angles are equal and the sides of one figure are in proportion to the sides of the other. Scale drawings produce similar shapes.

All pairs that can be made with the three rectangles below are similar; their sides are in proportion and their angles are equal. If you double the lengths of all of the sides of the 3 by 2 rectangle, you get a 6 by 4 rectangle. If you multiply the sides of the 6 by 4 rectangle by 1.5, you get a 9 by 6 rectangle. You also get a 9 by 6 rectangle by tripling the sides of the 3 by 2 rectangle. As long as you multiply all of the sides of a rectangle by the same factor, you get a similar rectangle.

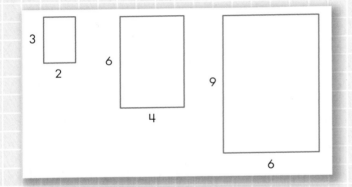

The next three rectangles illustrate one pair of rectangles that is similar and other pairs of rectangles that are not similar. The first two rectangles are similar, but neither is similar to the third. You cannot multiply the dimensions of either of these rectangles (3 by 2 or 6 by 4) by the same factor to get a 9 by 8 rectangle.

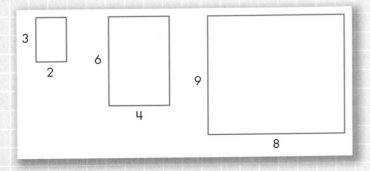

Students often erroneously believe that having the same shape means having the same name. For example, a "skinny" rectangle and a "fat" rectangle may mistakenly be thought of as having the same shape just because they are both rectangles. In geometry, figures that are considered to have the same shape must be in proportion like figures that are duplicated, reduced, or enlarged by a copy machine. So "having the same shape" and "being similar" are equivalent, but "having the same shape" and "being described by the same shape name" are not.

Any regular polygon is similar to any other regular polygon that has the same number of sides. For example, any regular, or equilateral, triangle has three 60° angles and equal sides. If you take an equilateral triangle and enlarge it—or shrink it—to any other size equilateral triangle, it will still have three 60° angles and equal sides. It will be similar to the original one. Likewise, if you enlarge or shrink a regular pentagon (five equal sides and five equal angles of 108°) to any other size regular pentagon, the new figure will be similar to the original one. Thus the shape of the Pentagon building near Washington, D.C., is similar to any regular pentagon.

The activities in this unit build ideas about similarity without requiring formal use of proportion. Other terms, such as *same shape* and *scale* are used to discuss the idea of mathematical similarity. When the term *similar* is introduced to students, alert them to the distinction between the mathematical meaning and its general meaning. If students need additional help understanding the idea of similar figures, show examples of similar rectangles and compare them to rectangles that are not similar.

Building Larger Similar Figures

When students begin making similar figures for their Similarity Posters, there are several different ways they can construct these shapes, depending on how many sides their original figure has.

Shapes with Three and Four Sides

For many triangles and quadrilaterals, one way to make similar figures is by tessellating the original shape. For example, given a shape made with Power Polygons A and E, students could make a similar larger shape with four copies of the original shape.

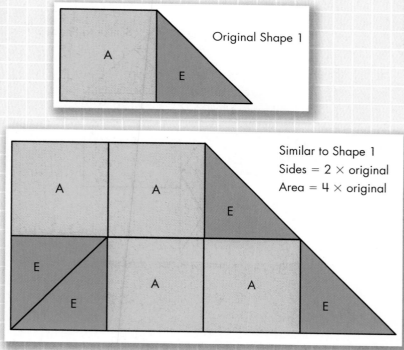

Original Shape 1

Similar to Shape 1
Sides = 2 × original
Area = 4 × original

Students may also find ways to use different pieces to make similar shapes for A and E. For example, they might make a smaller similar shape with B and F.

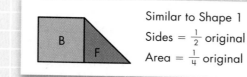

Similar to Shape 1
Sides = $\frac{1}{2}$ original
Area = $\frac{1}{4}$ original

Shapes with More than Four Sides

Strategies other than tessellating are used to make larger similar figures when the original shape has more than four sides. Either different pieces need to be used, or multiples of the individual shapes must be used. Consider this original:

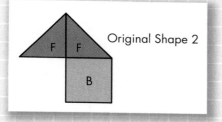

Original Shape 2

Using different pieces, students could construct a similar shape, as shown here:

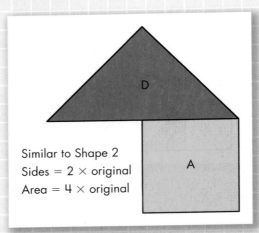

Similar to Shape 2
Sides = 2 × original
Area = 4 × original

Students could also use four of each of the individual shapes (B, F, F) to construct a similar shape with four times the area.

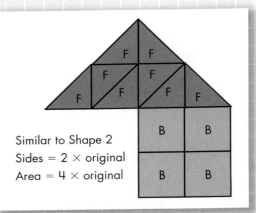

Similar to Shape 2
Sides = 2 × original
Area = 4 × original

Starting with the original shape below, students could not use four figures of the same shape to construct a similar figure. Instead, they could use four of each individual shape (D, G, J, and A) to make larger, similar pieces that would go together to make a shape similar to the original and four times as large.

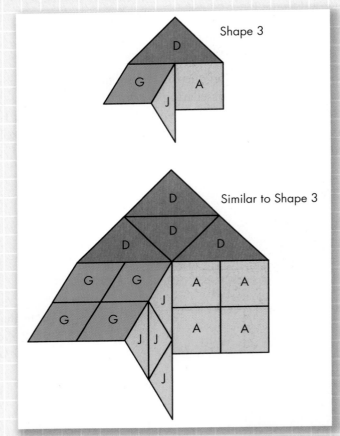

Shape 3

Similar to Shape 3

End-of-Unit Assessment

Problem 1

Benchmark addressed:

Benchmark 2: Use known angle sizes to determine the sizes of other angles (30 degrees, 45 degrees, 60 degrees, 90 degrees, 120 degrees, and 150 degrees).

In order to meet the benchmark, students' work should show that they can:

- Identify each of the five angles in the pentagon;

- Accurately find the measure of two of the angles in the pentagon by using knowledge of angles in the Power Polygons.

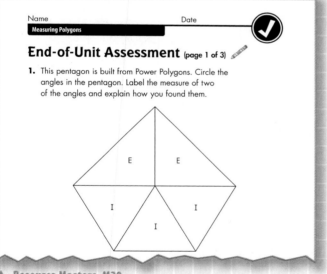

▲ **Resource Masters, M20**

It is expected that most students will continue to use the Power Polygon pieces as reference for finding the measure of the angles in this new polygon. At this point, many students have enough experience with the measures of some of the Power Polygon angles, such as that an equilateral triangle has three 60° angles, or an isosceles right triangle has one 90° and two 45° angles, that they can now use these as "benchmark" angles, and therefore do not need to explain these measures each time they use them.

Meeting the Benchmark

Students who meet the benchmark can identify and accurately find the measure of each angle they select. In order to do this, students distinguish between the angles of the Power Polygons used to build the pentagon, and the angles in the pentagon created. Their explanations include what references they used to find the measures (such as Power Polygon pieces) and how they combined angle measures to find the size of the 105° angle, which does not match any of the Power Polygon pieces.

Alicia uses two polygon shapes as references to prove the measure of the two 120 degree angles. She uses the green equilateral triangle (shape N) to find that the angles in shape I are also each 60 degrees.

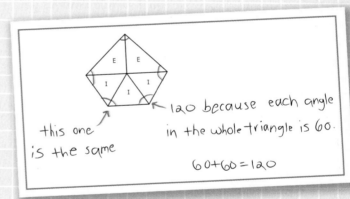

Alicia's Work

Deon also meets the benchmark because he has correctly identified all of the angles in the pentagon and found the measure of at least two angles (he actually has found the measures of all of the angles). It seems that Deon recognizes the angles in each of the Power Polygon pieces and that these have become benchmarks for him to use to construct other angles.

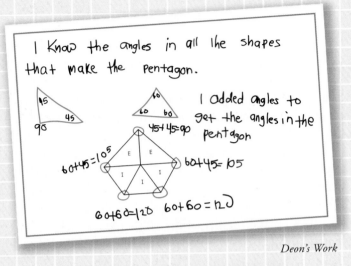

I know the angles in all the shapes that make the pentagon.

I added angles to get the angles in the pentagon

45 + 45 = 90

60 + 45 = 105   60 + 45 = 105

60 + 60 = 120   60 + 60 = 120

Deon's Work

Lourdes used knowledge of the measure of the angles in the equilateral triangle to find the measure of one of the 120° angles. She used knowledge of 90° angles in a square by matching one angle in the square to the top angle in the pentagon and found that it was equal. While Lourdes did not circle all five angles in the pentagon, she clearly understands what the angles are and correctly identifies the measure of two of these angles. Ask Lourdes to identify the other three angles in the pentagon.

90 I matched this with a corner of the square

60 + 60 = 120

I know all the angles are 60 degrees in all those bottom triangles

Lourdes's Work

Partially Meeting the Benchmark

Some students confuse the angles in each Power Polygon piece for the angles in the pentagon, they may find only one of the angles in the pentagon, or their explanations may be incomplete.

Tavon correctly identifies the 90° angle in the pentagon and then also identifies a 90° angle in the center of the pentagon made by the right angle in the right isosceles triangle. While both of these right angles are correctly labeled, Tavon should be asked to look back at his work and consider how many sides and how many angles are in a pentagon and which angles make up the pentagon. It may be that Tavon does not know how to find the measure of any angle other than one that is 90°. If this is the case, he needs to return to work on finding different angles with the Power Polygons.

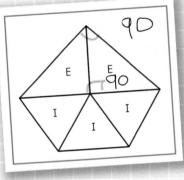

Tavon's Work

Mercedes uses correct reasoning to identify one of the 120° angles by adding two 60° angles she knows from the equilateral triangle. She then finds part of one of the 105° angles by writing 60 + _____. She knows that one piece is equal to 60 but does not know how to find the other piece. Mercedes should return to work that helps her identify the measure of angles in the Power Polygons so she can create more angle "benchmarks"; for example, recognizing the 90° and 45° angles in a right isosceles triangle.

Mercedes's Work

Talisha correctly identifies all of the angles in the pentagon, but incorrectly assumes that it is a regular pentagon and all the angles are equal, so she only finds the measure of one of the angles. Encourage Talisha to look carefully at the length of the sides and use her Power Polygon pieces to compare the size of each angle. She may be able to return to her work and find the measurement of another angle.

Talisha's Work

Not Meeting the Benchmark

Students who do not meet the benchmark confuse the angles in each Power Polygon piece for the angles in the pentagon and do not correctly find any of the angle measurements in the pentagon.

Terrence circles every angle in all of the Power Polygons in the figure and finds the measure of two Power Polygon angles.

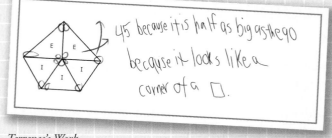

Terrence's Work

Hana correctly identifies the angle in the equilateral triangle, but then incorrectly adds on another 30 because the rest of the angle looks to her like half of 60. Hana is relying on a visual reference instead of finding the actual angle measurement. She clearly does not check to see whether what she thinks is a 90° angle matches up with an angle in a rectangle. She also does not identify all of the angles in the pentagon.

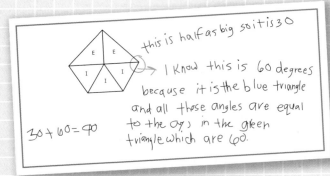

Hana's Work

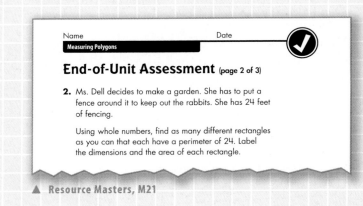

▲ **Resource Masters, M21**

It is important to make sure that these students know how to identify angles in polygons. Have students make many different polygons with the Power Polygons and help them identify the angles in the new polygons. Also, these students need more practice with angle measurement in the Power Polygons. Have students work again on *Student Activity Book* pages 17–19. Ask questions such as:

Can you find all of the combinations of angles that equal 90°? If combined they equal 90°, how many degrees are in each of the angles? If these two are each half of 90°, how many degrees is one of the angles?

Problem 2

Benchmark addressed:

Benchmark 3: Determine the perimeter and area of rectangles.

In order to meet the benchmark, students' work should show that they can:

- Distinguish between the measure of perimeter and area;

- Accurately identify at least three different rectangles that have a perimeter of 24.

Meeting the Benchmark

Students who meet the benchmark understand that their task is to create at least three rectangles with a constant perimeter of 24, but a changing area. Using whole numbers, there are six possible rectangles that have a perimeter of 24 (1×11, 2×10, 3×9, 4×8, 5×7, 6×6). Some students may find all of these rectangles by starting with a square and moving to the longest and narrowest, or the reverse. (Note that some students may not understand that a square is a rectangle; this error should be noted and corrected at a later time.) Other students may find all or a few rectangles by trial and error, finding numbers for the dimensions that they know add up to 24. At this point in Grade 5, most students should be able to find the area of a rectangle by multiplying the dimensions or skip counting by rows or columns (rather than by counting every square unit inside the rectangle).

Nora found all six rectangles by starting with the "longest and skinniest." Once she found rectangles with a perimeter of 24, she multiplied each dimension to find the area. She added a comment about which garden she thinks Ms. Dell should use.

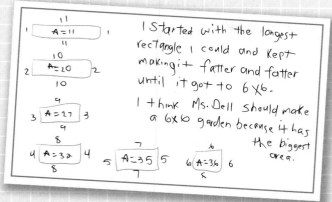

Nora's Work

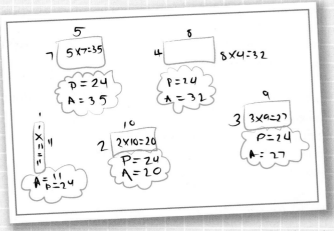

Hana's Work

Samantha drew four different rectangles, and all the perimeters and areas are correctly labeled. She drew each unit in her rectangles but she counted each row to find the area.

Partially Meeting the Benchmark

Students who partially meet the benchmark may find only one or two rectangles that have a perimeter of 24, or they may incorrectly identify area and perimeter.

Zachary shows all of the computation he did to find the perimeter and area of each of only two rectangles. His calculations are correct, and he shows that he knows the difference between the measurements of area and perimeter.

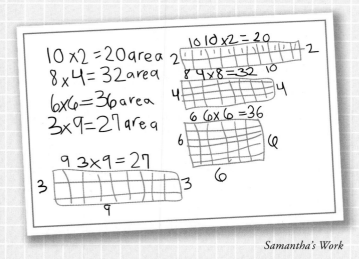

Samantha's Work

Hana found all the possible rectangles that have a perimeter of 24, except the 6 × 6 square. Hana should be asked whether she can find any more, or be shown a 6 × 6 square and asked whether it is a rectangle to make sure she knows that squares are rectangles.

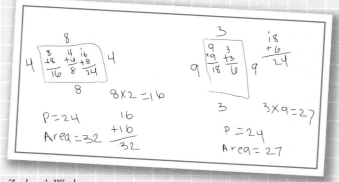

Zachary's Work

Georgia mixes up area and perimeter, but her calculations are accurate. Georgia should be asked to check her work to see whether she notices her mistake. If she does not yet know which measurements are identified as area and perimeter, she should be asked to identify situations in which perimeter would be useful (fencing, a border around a bulletin board) and those in which area would be useful (painting a wall, covering a book). This will help her connect the calculations she is doing with situations where you find perimeter or area.

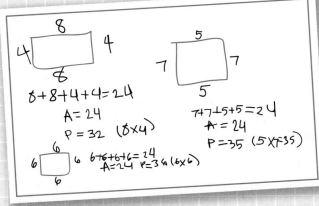

Georgia's Work

Not Meeting the Benchmark

Students who do not meet the benchmark may present incomplete work. These students need to be questioned to identify what they may or may not understand.

Walter simply drew two rectangles that each have a perimeter of 24, but did not include area measurements.

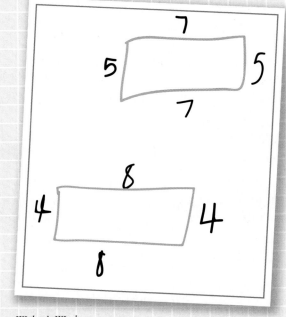

Walter's Work

It may be apparent in the work of some students that they are unclear about how to find area and perimeter. Ask these students whether they can identify the measures of area and perimeter in some rectangles on grid paper. Then have students return to finding the area and perimeter of several different rectangles.

Problem 3

Benchmark addressed:

Benchmark 4: Identify mathematically similar polygons.

In order to meet the benchmark, students' work should show that they can:

- Correctly identify similar polygons;

- Explain what makes polygons similar to each other;

- Draw a rectangle that is similar to the original rectangle.

Name _____ Date _____
Measuring Polygons

End-of-Unit Assessment (page 3 of 3)

3. Consider the following rectangles:

Rectangle A   Rectangle B

A. Are the two rectangles similar? Explain why you think so.

B. If you do not think they are similar, draw a rectangle that is similar to rectangle A.

▲ **Resource Masters, M22**

Meeting the Benchmark

Students meeting the benchmark recognize that rectangles A and B are not similar because the sides are not proportional. It is expected that students' explanations show they understand that the sides of similar figures have to be proportional. In this case, they must notice that the width of rectangle B is three times as long as rectangle A, while the length is only two times as long. (While similar shapes must also have the same angles, students do not have to explicitly mention angle size because these are both rectangles.) These students also correctly draw a similar rectangle for Problem 3b.

Rachel recognizes that for figures to be similar, the angles have to be the same and the sides have to be multiplied by the same number. Rachel explicitly states that the "top" of rectangle B is "three times longer," but the "side" is only "two times longer." Rachel is also able to draw a rectangle similar to rectangle A with dimensions that are three times longer.

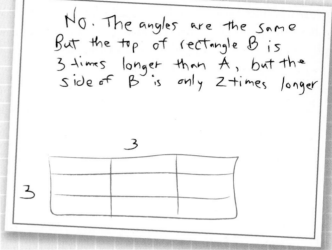

Rachel's Work

Renaldo also meets the benchmark. He recognizes that the growth in rectangle B is not proportional; that rectangle B is "too long." He correctly draws a rectangle similar to rectangle A with dimensions that are two times longer.

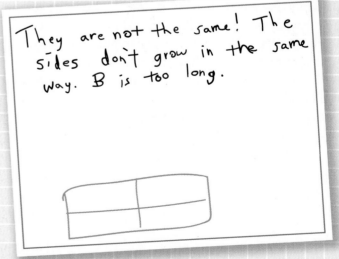

Renaldo's Work

Partially Meeting the Benchmark

Some students do not have a complete explanation as to why the rectangles are not similar, or are unable to draw a similar rectangle.

Tyler's explanation is incomplete. He recognizes the rectangles are not similar, but his explanation only states that the rectangles "don't look like the same shape." It is unclear whether Tyler can articulate why the rectangles do not have the same shape. Tyler is able to draw a rectangle similar to rectangle A with dimensions three times longer, so he partially meets the benchmark.

No — they don't look like they are the same shape.

Tyler's Work

Shandra recognizes the rectangles are not similar, and indicates that rectangle B is "too long." This indicates she understands that similar figures need to have the same shape. However, Shandra is unable to draw a rectangle similar to rectangle A. Only one dimension of her rectangle is doubled; the other dimension remains the same. Shandra will benefit from using the *LogoPaths* software to create similar shapes and determine whether two pictured shapes are similar.

No they are not. Rectangle B is made up of too many rectangles — it's too long.

Shandra's Work

Not Meeting the Benchmark

Some students think the two rectangles are similar. They do not notice, or are not aware, that in order for shapes to be similar, the sides have to be equally proportional.

Cecilia says the figures are similar because they are both rectangles and "look the same." Cecilia still seems to think that shape refers to the name of the figure. Cecilia will benefit from using the *LogoPaths* software to create similar shapes and determine whether two pictured shapes in the Polygon Pairs activity are similar.

Yes! They are both rectangles and look the same.

Cecilia's Work

Finding Angle Measures of Power Polygons

This class has been working on *Student Activity Book* pages 17–19. The teacher decided to assign one or two shapes to each group, and now they are presenting their strategies to the class. In this class, students are encouraged to show more than one way to find the angle measures. (In the illustrations below, note that the shaded areas are parts of the shapes that are covered by other shapes.)

Teacher: Tyler and Martin, could you tell us how you found the angles for J?

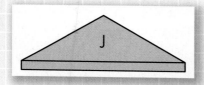

Martin: We used shape L because it fits on half of J. The smallest angle of L is 30°, so that means the two small angles of J are 30° too because they're the same.

Tyler: Then we knew the other angle of L, that's not a right angle, is 60°, and put those two together, you get 120°. So that's the big angle in J.

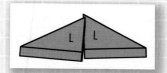

Teacher: Mercedes' group, you worked on shape M. What did you find out?

Mercedes: For M, we used J to measure. The bigger angles, the obtuse ones, in M and J matched, and we already figured out they were 120°. For the other two angles in M, it takes two of them to fit exactly in the 120° in J. So divide it by 2 and get 60.

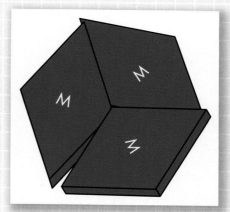

Alicia: Just like you put those eight triangles together, we can put these fat angles in M together and make a whole piece, like a circle, with three. So that makes the angle 120, because three times 120 is 360.

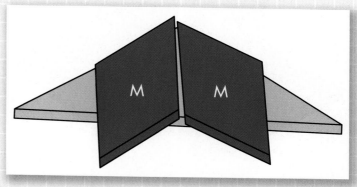

Zachary: And see [moving six of the small angles on M together into a circle]—here there are six. And 360 divided by 6 makes 60 degrees.

Terrence: Our group worked on G, and look [showing rhombuses M and G]—these are the same shape, aren't they? G is just bigger. The angles are the same for both, the sides are just bigger. See if you do this [laying shape M on top of shape G, aligning the 120° angles first and then the 60° angles], the angles are the same. Also you could fit four of the small ones inside the big one. So the angles are the same but the sides are different.

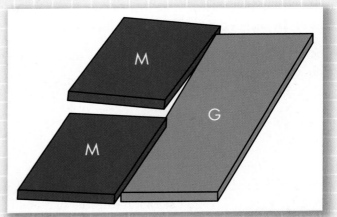

In the process of finding angle measures in the individual shapes, students are finding relationships among Power Polygons. Many students find the same-size angles in different shapes, and use that information to help them reason about other angles. Terrence notices that some pairs of shapes are similar—that is, they have the same angles, and their corresponding sides are in proportion to each other. Students will explore the idea of similarity in Investigation 3 of this unit.

Doubling the Dimensions

In Investigation 2, Session 2.2, students have been considering how the perimeter and area change when the sides of a square are doubled. On *Student Activity Book* pages 31–32 they are asked to explain what is happening to these two measurements. In this class discussion, the teacher wants to focus on connecting numerical explanations with explanations that are based on visual representations.

Teacher: What happens to the area of a square when the side lengths are doubled?

Tyler: It increases times 4. With the 2-inch square, the area was 4 square inches. With the 4-inch square, the area was 16 square inches. That means it's four times bigger. The same thing happened with the 3-inch square—it was 9 square inches, but then when the sides were doubled the area was 36 square inches. That's four times bigger too.

Teacher: Does everyone agree with Tyler?

The students agree that this is true.

Teacher: Who can explain why this happens?

Hana: I'm not really sure how to say this, but it's like how multiplication makes things a lot bigger. Since both sides are two times longer, and you multiply to find area, the area is going to be four times bigger. It's hard to explain.

Teacher: Is there anyone who can help out Hana? Do you understand what she's trying to say?

Renaldo: It is hard. But it makes sense. It's too confusing with the 2-inch square because there are too many twos. But if you think about the 3-inch square, you want to make the sides two times longer, right? [Renaldo goes to the board and draws two squares. He labels the dimensions of the first square as 3 by 3.] See, to make the sides twice as long you "times 2." [He writes 3×2 next to each dimension of the larger square.] To find area, you multiply the side times the side, so this is like doing $3 \times 2 \times 3 \times 2$—so it shows the area is going to be four times larger.

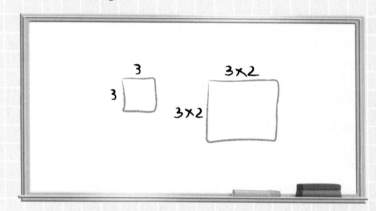

The teacher realizes these explanations are helping some students, and wants to include a more concrete representation to help students who are having difficulty visualizing how the area grows.

Teacher: Did anyone build or draw the squares to help understand why the area increases four times?

Olivia: Yeah, we drew it. Can I come up to the board? . . . [She draws the 3 by 3 square.] First we drew the 3 by 3 square. Then we knew we had to double the sides, so first we put another 3 by 3 square below the first one, then we put another to the right. That didn't give us a square, so we put one more in the second row. So now it's a 6-inch square, and you can see how the area is four times bigger, because we used four of the 3-inch squares.

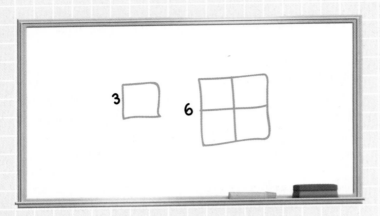

Teacher: Any questions for Olivia?. . . Everyone figured out that the area quadrupled, and what Olivia did shows us very well how the area increased four times. Now what about perimeter? What happens with perimeter?

Lourdes: The perimeter only doubles. For a 2-inch square, the perimeter is 8 inches, and for the 4-inch square, it's 16 inches. Same for the 3-inch square. It goes from 12 inches to 24 inches.

Teacher: I think everyone agrees that when you double the side lengths, the perimeter doubles. Who can explain why it only doubles, and doesn't quadruple like area does?

Samantha: When you put the squares together like Olivia did, you lose some of the perimeter of each square. So even though you're using 4 squares to make the new square, the perimeter gets lost.

Zachary: Gets lost? I'm not sure what that means.

Samantha goes to the board and points to where the edges of the squares Olivia drew are now inside the larger square.

Samantha: See, not every side of the square becomes part of the perimeter of the new square.

Terrence: I thought about it another way. [He goes to the board and points at the squares Olivia drew. He darkens the outline of the first square.] Look; this is the original square and perimeter. [On the second square, he darkens in the top left corner, and the bottom right corner.] See, it's like if you stretched the square out to make it bigger. This perimeter is still there, and then you just add up the other. He points to the other two corners of the square. So the perimeter only doubles.

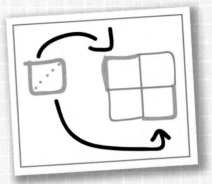

The teacher knows that many students can quickly identify a pattern and solve these problems numerically, which is fine. In this Investigation, she also wants students to continue building their conceptual understanding of perimeter and area. To help them do this, she has the students build each of the squares with square tiles. She also encourages them to use square tiles or a drawing to understand and explain the ways in which perimeter and area change as the dimensions of the squares change.

Building Similar Hexagons

In this Grade 5 class, students begin working with mathematically similar shapes by building similar polygons using Power Polygon pieces B, C, N, J, M, and O. Similar figures can be built for each of these shapes by simply repeating the original shapes (e.g., the second figure for triangle J can be built using four triangle Js, and the third by using nine triangle Js). Students are then asked to build hexagons similar to hexagon H. Unlike the previous pieces they studied, they now have to use Power Polygon pieces other than hexagon H. The teacher circulates and observes students as they work in pairs on this activity.

The teacher stops to watch Hana and Mitch. A hexagon H is on the table in front of them, and they sit, staring at it.

Teacher: You two look deep in thought. What are you thinking so hard about?

Hana: We just can't figure out what to do. First we put two hexagons together, but that won't work.

Teacher: Why won't that work?

Hana: It just won't. The hexagons don't fit together like the other polygons did. If you put the two hexagons together, there are spaces, and then each side is more than two times as long.

Mitch: So we don't know what to do!

Teacher: Have you looked at the chart? [The teacher points to the chart completed earlier in the session, "Ways to make Hexagon H."] Earlier, we found different polygon pieces that were the same size as this hexagon. Can that help you?

Mitch: Let's see, we know the second hexagon has to have sides twice as long. Maybe this rhombus? [He places rhombus M below the hexagon.]

Hana: And look! We could put the triangle next to it. [She places triangle N next to rhombus M.]

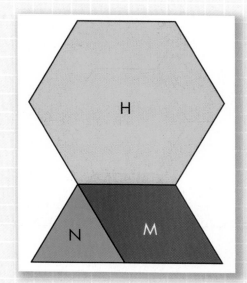

Mitch: Hana, you know what? That's the same as one trapezoid. Maybe we can use trapezoids the rest of the way.

Teacher: It looks like you have a start, so that's good. Look at what you have so far. If your rhombus and triangle make one side of the similar hexagon, is it two times longer than the original hexagon? How do you know? As you continue to build, also think about how you can be sure the angles are the same size as the original.

Hana picks up another hexagon H and compares the length of the side, first matching it up with the base of the rhombus, and then the base of the triangle.

Hana: Looks like twice as long to me!

Next, the teacher stops and watches Mercedes, Felix, and Tamira. The three students are looking at the figure they have built, and trying to determine what to do next.

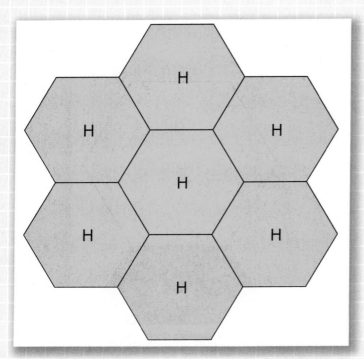

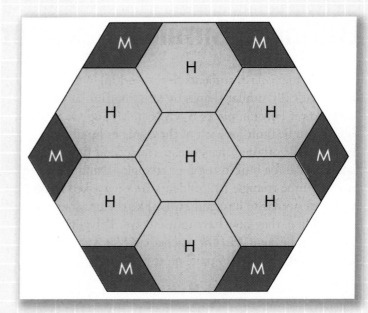

Teacher: I see you made another hexagon. Is it similar to hexagon H? How do you know?

Mercedes takes another hexagon H and compares each angle and tells the group that they are the same. Tamira takes the hexagon from her, and standing up, uses a visual method (closing one eye and moving the hexagon back and forth to see if it "matches" the hexagon on the table). She tells the group that the hexagons match.

Teacher: It sounds like you're convinced that these two hexagons are similar. How many times longer is each side of the hexagon you built? Two? Three? Four?

Mercedes: I think it's two times bigger, because it's the second hexagon we built.

Felix: I was thinking that too, but it doesn't look right. [He pauses.] I know! We already know each side has the same length as one hexagon, because it's made of hexagons. But what about the rhombuses?

Mercedes: We can just use a side of the hexagon to see how much longer the new hexagon is.

Mercedes takes a hexagon H and matches it carefully to each side of the larger hexagon. She counts softly to herself, "1, 2, 3." Soon, Felix and Tamira join her, chanting "1, 2, 3," as she measures each side.

Mercedes: Now what do we do? We can't keep adding hexagons. I think we could do the same thing forever and it still wouldn't make a hexagon!

Felix: We have to figure out a way to make this shape a hexagon. It looks like we could put a trapezoid here at the bottom. [Felix places a trapezoid to the right of the bottom hexagon.]

Tamira: That won't work—the edge sticks out, so it's not a hexagon. What about trying the rhombus?

The students see that rhombus M fits, and excitedly fill in the rest of the hexagon.

Tamira: It's the third figure! The sides of this hexagon are three times longer than the one we started with!

Teacher: Hmmm, so I guess now you have two things to figure out. What is the area of this third figure, if hexagon H is the unit of measure. And remember, you have to figure out how to build the second figure!

In order to do this activity, students need to understand that similar shapes do not have to be the same size, but they have to have the same shape—that is, they have to be to scale. Building similar shapes involves looking carefully at each side of the shape and at each angle, and then comparing both to the original. Since a similar hexagon cannot be created by simply adding more of the same shape, this task poses a new challenge for students. Are the angles the same size? Are all the sides proportional? Can you show that by matching up an angle or side of the original hexagon or by looking carefully at the shape from above? As the teacher watches students work, she is careful not to intercede too soon or give hints that are too obvious. As she works with students, she also questions them to make certain they can explain how they know the angles are the same size and how many times the side lengths have increased.

Student Math Handbook

The *Student Math Handbook* pages related to this unit are pictured on the following pages. This book is designed to be used flexibly: as a resource for students doing classwork, as a book students can take home for reference while doing homework and playing math games with their families, and as a reference for families to better understand the work their children are doing in class.

When students take the *Student Math Handbook* home, they and their families can discuss these pages together to reinforce or enhance students' understanding of the mathematical concepts and games in this unit.

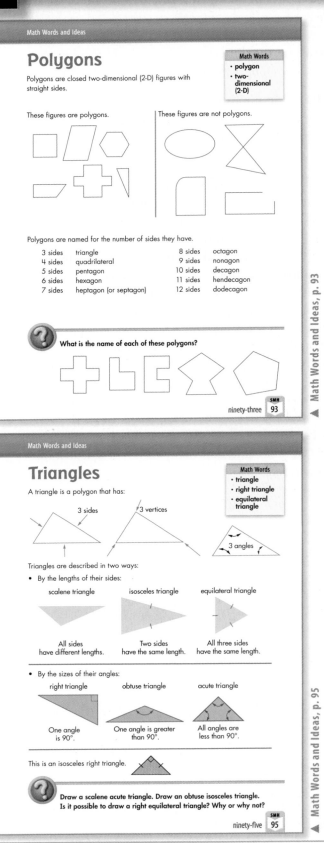

Math Words and Ideas, p. 93

Math Words and Ideas

Polygons

Polygons are closed two-dimensional (2-D) figures with straight sides.

Math Words
- polygon
- two-dimensional (2-D)

These figures are polygons.

These figures are not polygons.

Polygons are named for the number of sides they have.

3 sides	triangle	8 sides	octagon
4 sides	quadrilateral	9 sides	nonagon
5 sides	pentagon	10 sides	decagon
6 sides	hexagon	11 sides	hendecagon
7 sides	heptagon (or septagon)	12 sides	dodecagon

What is the name of each of these polygons?

ninety-three **93**

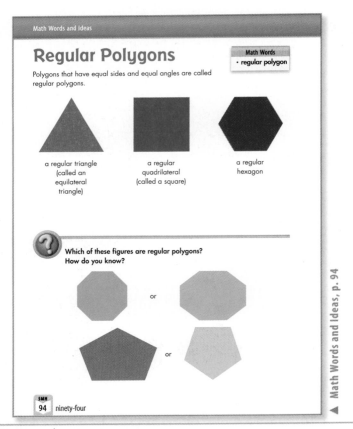

Math Words and Ideas, p. 94

Math Words and Ideas

Regular Polygons

Polygons that have equal sides and equal angles are called regular polygons.

Math Words
- regular polygon

a regular triangle (called an equilateral triangle)

a regular quadrilateral (called a square)

a regular hexagon

Which of these figures are regular polygons? How do you know?

or

or

94 ninety-four

Math Words and Ideas

Triangles

A triangle is a polygon that has:

Math Words
- triangle
- right triangle
- equilateral triangle

3 sides

3 vertices

3 angles

Triangles are described in two ways:

- By the lengths of their sides:

scalene triangle

isosceles triangle

equilateral triangle

All sides have different lengths.

Two sides have the same length.

All three sides have the same length.

- By the sizes of their angles:

right triangle

obtuse triangle

acute triangle

One angle is 90°.

One angle is greater than 90°.

All angles are less than 90°.

This is an isosceles right triangle.

Draw a scalene acute triangle. Draw an obtuse isosceles triangle. Is it possible to draw a right equilateral triangle? Why or why not?

ninety-five **95**

Math Words and Ideas, p. 95

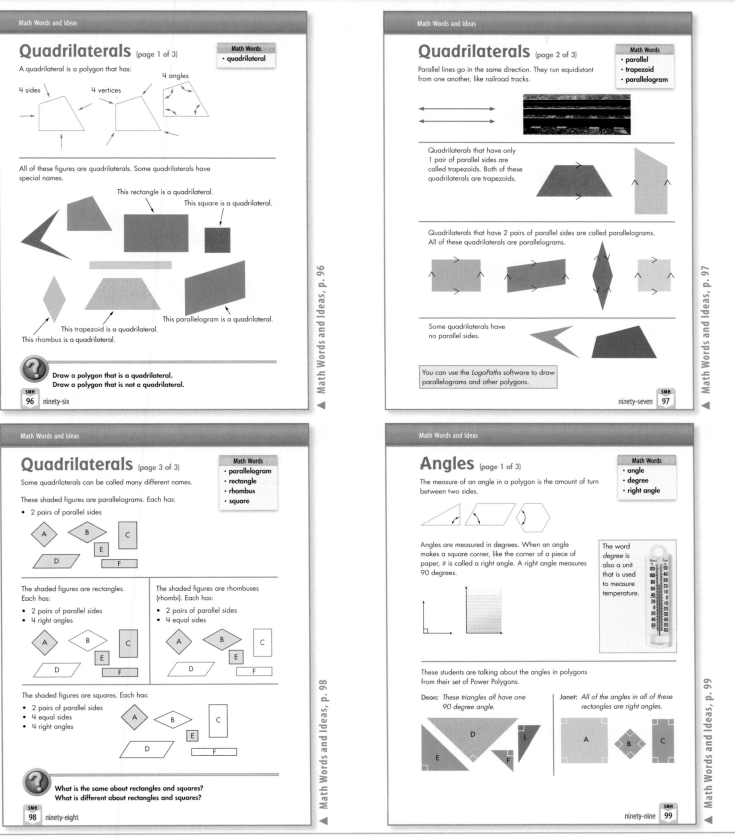

Math Words and Ideas

Quadrilaterals (page 1 of 3)

Math Words
• quadrilateral

A quadrilateral is a polygon that has:

4 sides   4 vertices   4 angles

All of these figures are quadrilaterals. Some quadrilaterals have special names.

This rectangle is a quadrilateral.

This square is a quadrilateral.

This parallelogram is a quadrilateral.

This trapezoid is a quadrilateral.

This rhombus is a quadrilateral.

Draw a polygon that is a quadrilateral.
Draw a polygon that is not a quadrilateral.

SMH 96 ninety-six

▲ Math Words and Ideas, p. 96

Math Words and Ideas

Quadrilaterals (page 2 of 3)

Math Words
• parallel
• trapezoid
• parallelogram

Parallel lines go in the same direction. They run equidistant from one another, like railroad tracks.

Quadrilaterals that have only 1 pair of parallel sides are called trapezoids. Both of these quadrilaterals are trapezoids.

Quadrilaterals that have 2 pairs of parallel sides are called parallelograms. All of these quadrilaterals are parallelograms.

Some quadrilaterals have no parallel sides.

You can use the *LogoPaths* software to draw parallelograms and other polygons.

ninety-seven SMH 97

▲ Math Words and Ideas, p. 97

Math Words and Ideas

Quadrilaterals (page 3 of 3)

Math Words
• parallelogram
• rectangle
• rhombus
• square

Some quadrilaterals can be called many different names.

These shaded figures are parallelograms. Each has:
• 2 pairs of parallel sides

A B C
E
D F

The shaded figures are rectangles. Each has:
• 2 pairs of parallel sides
• 4 right angles

A B C
E
D F

The shaded figures are rhombuses (rhombi). Each has:
• 2 pairs of parallel sides
• 4 equal sides

A B C
E
D F

The shaded figures are squares. Each has:
• 2 pairs of parallel sides
• 4 equal sides
• 4 right angles

A B C
E
D F

What is the same about rectangles and squares?
What is different about rectangles and squares?

SMH 98 ninety-eight

▲ Math Words and Ideas, p. 98

Math Words and Ideas

Angles (page 1 of 3)

Math Words
• angle
• degree
• right angle

The measure of an angle in a polygon is the amount of turn between two sides.

Angles are measured in degrees. When an angle makes a square corner, like the corner of a piece of paper, it is called a right angle. A right angle measures 90 degrees.

The word *degree* is also a unit that is used to measure temperature.

These students are talking about the angles in polygons from their set of Power Polygons.

Deon: *These triangles all have one 90 degree angle.*

D L
E F

Janet: *All of the angles in all of these rectangles are right angles.*

A B C

ninety-nine SMH 99

▲ Math Words and Ideas, p. 99

Math Words and Ideas

Angles (page 2 of 3)

Hana: *None of the angles in this trapezoid is 90 degrees.*

This angle is less than 90 degrees. It is smaller than the corner of the paper.

An acute angle is smaller than a right angle.

This angle is greater than 90 degrees. It is larger than the corner of the paper.

An obtuse angle is larger than a right angle.

Look at these figures:

Do you see any 90 degree angles? If so, where?
Do you see any angles less than 90 degrees? If so, where?
Do you see any angles greater than 90 degrees? If so, where?

SMH **100** one hundred

◀ Math Words and Ideas, p. 100

Math Words and Ideas

Angles (page 3 of 3)

How many degrees are in this angle?

How do you know?

Mitch: *I can use two of these triangles to make a square.*

$45 + 45 = 90$

These two angles together make 90°. They are equal, so each angle measures 45°.

How many degrees are in this angle?

How do you know?

Alicia: *When I put three of the hexagons together, three of the angles in the middle make a circle.*

You can use the *LogoPaths* software to solve problems about angles.

$360 ÷ 3 = 120$

The circle has 360°, so each angle measures 120°.

How many degrees are in this angle?
How do you know?

SMH **101** one hundred one

◀ Math Words and Ideas, p. 101

Math Words and Ideas

Perimeter and Area

Lourdes and her father are building a patio. The patio is made up of 1-foot square tiles. They are also building a fence around the patio. Here is a sketch of their patio design.

Lourdes and her father need to use two different measurements for their patio project.

12 feet

8 feet

Perimeter is the length of the border of a figure.

Perimeter is measured in linear units such as centimeters, inches, or feet.

Area is the measure of a 2-D surface, for example the amount of flat space a figure covers.

Area is measured in square units, such as square centimeters or square feet.

What is the perimeter of the patio? How long will the fence be?

Cecilia:
$8 + 12 + 8 + 12 = 40$
perimeter = 40 feet
The fence will be **40 feet** long

What is the area of the patio? How many square tiles do they need?

Mitch:
$8 × 12 = 96$
Area = 96 square feet
They need **96 tiles**.

5
4
A

10
2
B

9
3
C

Which two rectangles have the same area?
Which two rectangles have the same perimeter?

SMH **102** one hundred two

◀ Math Words and Ideas, p. 102

Math Words and Ideas

Similarity (page 1 of 2)

Two figures are similar if they have exactly the same shape. They do not have to be the same size.

Samantha and Mercedes looked for similar shapes in their set of Power Polygons.

Samantha: *These two triangles are similar.*

They are both isosceles right triangles. Each triangle has one 90° angle and two 45° angles.

The sides of triangle E are twice as long as the corresponding sides of triangle F.

45° 45° F 45°

E

45°

Mercedes: *These two squares are similar.*

They both have four right angles.

The sides of square B are half as long as the corresponding sides of square A.

B A

SMH **103** one hundred three

◀ Math Words and Ideas, p. 103

Similarity (page 2 of 2)

Alex compared rectangle C to a rectangle he built using four square B pieces from the Power Polygon set.

Alex: *These two rectangles are NOT similar.*

Even though they both have four right angles, the shape isn't the same.

The larger rectangle is twice as tall as the smaller rectangle, but it isn't twice as wide. Both rectangles are the same width.

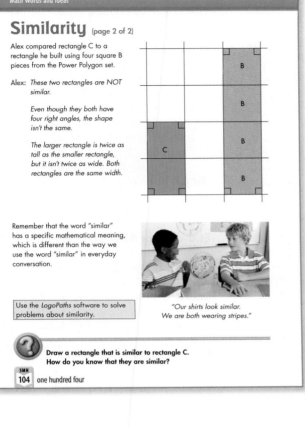

Remember that the word "similar" has a specific mathematical meaning, which is different than the way we use the word "similar" in everyday conversation.

Use the *LogoPaths* software to solve problems about similarity.

"Our shirts look similar. We are both wearing stripes."

Draw a rectangle that is similar to rectangle C. How do you know that they are similar?

SMH
104 one hundred four

▲ Math Words and Ideas, p. 104

Index